Circumcision in Islam

Abu Bakr Abdu'r-Razzaq

DAR AL TAQWA LTD.

ISBN 1 870582 95 0

Translated by Aisha Bewley

Edited by Abdalhaqq Bewley and Muhammad 'Isa Waley

Production: Bookwork, Norwich
Cover Design by A. Negm

Published by:
Dar Al Taqwa Ltd.
7A, Melcombe Street
Baker Street
London
NW1 6AE
web: http://www.btinternet.com/~dar.altaqwa/newtaqwa. htm
email: dar.altaqwa@btinternet.com

Printed and Bound by- De-Luxe Printers,
London NW10 7NR.
website: http://www.de-luxe.com
email: printers@de-luxe.com

Table of Contents

**In the Name of God the Most
Merciful the Most Compassionate**

Preface

O Allah, we praise You with the thanks of one You have helped with Your success and We laud You with the glorification of one who has purchased Your wisdom in exchange for prattle and enjoyed a profitable exchange. We praise You, O Allah, with a praise which connects new blessings to old. We ask You for success by which we may be protected from all slips of the pen, both major and minor.

Infant circumcision, especially that of females, is one of those knotty topics which have been fiercely debated from ancient times and in various guises. It is a topic which has provoked dispute and almost continuous debate – among scholars and philosophers at one time and men of the Church and Jewish rabbis at another – and everyone offers an opinion formed on the basis of his own whims. Whoever follows his own whims is clearly misguided.

These disputes and arguments continued until the light of Islam illuminated the world with the Message of the Final Prophet and Messenger, represented by the Noble Qur'an, the Clear Book of Allah, which no falsehood enters from before or from behind, and which clarifies for mankind matters of this world and the *deen* in clear, explicit texts. Whoever holds to it is saved and guided to the Straight Path. Whoever is guided by anything else is misguided and misled.

The purifying *Sunna* of the Prophet came to make clear with examples any obscurity in the text of the Noble Qur'an. The question of circumcision is one of the first topics which was clarified by the pure *Sunna*. It removed all the uncertainties as to its legality and its rulings with regard to both male and female circumcision. The opinion of the Imams of Islamic *fiqh* is based on the guidance of the Book of Allah and the *Sunna* of His Messenger Muhammad, may Allah bless him and grant him peace.

Since the early 1950s several world conferences have been held to debate circumcision and many papers, magazine articles and books published about it. In May 1951 the magazine *ad-Duktur* dealt specifically with female circumcision. A number of doctors were asked for their opinion. Some of them followed their own bias, stating that female circumcision was a barbaric practice which caused grave psychological and social harm to girls. Others opposed the *Deen,* contending that nothing in the *Shari'a* requires circumcision and added – and they sinned by doing so – that there is nothing in the *hadiths* of the Prophet nor in the *fiqh* of the Imams that orders female circumcision.

Because of all this I consider it my duty as a Muslim with sincere concern for my *deen* and community to place before the Muslim family, reader and researcher this book which begins with a comparative study of circumcision in all divine and man-made laws and with a historical overview of the discussion and argument between scholars and philosophers, especially the Jews.

Then I will deal separately with the opinion of medical men and psychologists and sociologists among the Muslims and writers of other religions. I will follow that with the opinion of the *deen* as enunciated by eminent *fuqaha',* some of the best scholars of this time, such as Shaykh Ibrahim Hamrush, a great scholar and Chairman of the Fatwa Committee; Shaykh 'Abdu'l-Wahhab Khallaf, Professor of Shari'a in the Law College of Cairo; Shaykh 'Allam Nassar, the Mufti of Egypt; Shaykh Muhammad al-Banna, Deputy Minister for Religious Affairs; Shaykh Muhammad Ibrahim Salim, Head of the Higher Shari'a Court; Prof. Muhammad al-Laban; Imam Shaykh Mahmud Shaltut, Shaykh of al-Azhar; Shaykh Mahmud 'Arnus, Head of Shari'a Review; Dr. Zakariyya al-Birri, Head of the Department of Shari'a in the Law College of Cairo and Minister of Awqaf; and Dr. 'Abdu'r-Rahman al-'Adawi, professor in the College of Da'wa at al-Azhar University. The opinions of all them are taken from the Book and *Sunna* and the *ijtihad* of the righteous *Salaf*.

I have also appended a slightly abridged translation of Chapter Nine of *Tuhfat al-Mawdud fi Ahkam al-Mawlud* (The Gift of the Loving on Rulings concerning the Child) by Ibn al-Qayyim al-Jawziyya. This chapter has fourteen sections dealing with circumcision, beginning with the meaning of circumcision and its derivation and ending with a discussion about the circumcision of our Prophet Muhammad, may Allah bless him and grant him peace, and the wisdom by which people will be resurrected on the Day of Rising uncircumcised. Ibn al-Qayyim was a *faqih* with absolute *ijtihad* and the scholars of his time described him as "the *faqih* who has mastered all the sciences of Islam."

By this humble effort I have produced the first comprehensive book on this topic, clarifying the meaning of circumcision, its history and the opinion of science and medicine and the religion regarding it, and its effects from a psychological, social and moral perspective on the lives of both men and women and on society as a whole.

"Our Lord, do not take us to task if we forget or make a mistake. Our Lord, do not load us with such a burden as You loaded onto those before us. Our Lord, do not load us with that which we have not the strength to bear. And pardon us; and forgive us; and have mercy on us. You are our Master, so help us against the people of the rejectors." (2:286)

The one in need of his Lord's forgiveness
Abu Bakr 'Abdu'r-Razzaq

PART I
Historical Background

The Meaning of Circumcision in Holy Books and Dictionaries

One of the subjects which has occupied scholars and philosophers from ancient times and remained a matter of dispute until modern days is that of circumcision. Before we present the view of Islam, we will discuss various references made to it in the past mentioned in the Jewish and Christian Holy Books and in some Arabic and non-Arabic dictionaries.

In Deuteronomy 10:16 we find: "Circumcise therefore the foreskin of your heart, and be no more sticknecked." It also says elsewhere in Jeremiah 4:4, "Circumcise yourselves to the Lord, and take away the foreskins of your heart, ye men of Judah and inhabitants of Jerusalem." That is why we find that some scholars and philosophers define circumcision as symbolically removing the foreskin or covering over the heart to purify it from sin. For example, the scholar Tertullian and some of his partisans say, "Circumcision is not cutting part of the flesh and spilling blood: it is rather uncovering wisdom and spreading it."

In the *Dictionnaire Theologique*, we find that the derivation of the word circumcision is from the Latin 'circumcidere', which means to cut around. That is because circumcision is cutting around the prepuce. The Bureau of Jewish Sciences states that circumcision is cutting part of the foreskin.

The word circumcision has various forms in different languages. In Latin, the root is *circumcidere*. When it moved to Italian it became *circoncidere*, and in Spanish *circoncidare*, in English circumcision, in French *circoncision* and in German, the Latin root is abandoned and the word is *beschneiden*. In Aramaic it is *kheten* and in Hebrew *khatan* which means 'cut'. In Arabic, we find the word *khatn* and what is understood by *khitan* in Islam is purification and purifying.

7

This usage is applied to peoples who practise circumcision. As for the peoples who do not practise circumcision at all, they are called 'uncircumcised' (*arelim*) in Hebrew, as it is applied to the Palestinians. That accords with what is reported in I Samuel: "And Jonathan said to the young man that bare his armour, Come, and let us go over unto the garrison of these uncircumcised." (I Samuel 14:6) In the Book of Judges (14:3) "...thou goest to take a wife of the uncircumcised Philistines?"

We find that the Arabs in the *Jahiliyya* called those who were uncircumcised *'aqlaf'*, and *'aghral'* or *'aghlaf'*. They censured them and considered them inferior. That is the meaning designated by Semitic languages like Arabic, Hebrew, Aramaic and Syriac.

Among the Jews the word *hatan* is applied to a husband when he marries. That was because a Jewish man cannot marry a Jewish woman unless he is circumcised; so the word is applied to husbands in general. Although the word *hatan* is distinct from *khatn,* it seems that the two words are from the same root.

Khatn is used in Arabic in the following ways:

- Circumcision of boys and girls. The verb is used for both: the noun is *khitan* and *khitana*, and the circumcised person is *makhtun*. It is said that *khatn* is for men and *khafd* is for women, but *khitn* and *makhtun* apply to both male and female.

- *Khitana* is the job of the circumciser, *khatn* is the action of the *khatin* on the child, and *khitan* is the entire business.

- *Khitan* is the place of the circumcision in the penis and the excision of the skin covering the clitoris of the female.

Abu Mansur said, "It is the place of cutting in the male and female and it is the subject of the *hadith* related from the Noble Messenger, may Allah bless him and grant him peace, 'When the two circumcised parts meet, then *ghusl* is mandatory.' They are the place of cutting of the penis of the boy and the clitoris of the girl. Other nouns used for this are *i'dhar* and *khafd*. The meaning of

8

'their meeting' is the disappearance of the penis inside the vagina so that the circumcised parts touch."

This is what ash-Shafi'i said in his book: "The basis of circumcision is cutting. *Mukhatana* means relationship by marriage as a consequence of the meeting of the two circumcised parts."

The Origins of Circumcision and its Various Forms

It behoves us when discussing the origins of circumcision and what is mentioned about it, whether in the Holy Books or in the writings of historians, to first examine the various forms it can take.

There are basically two types of circumcision: physical circumcision, which is what we defined as removing the foreskin, and spiritual circumcision, which comprises the purification of souls and spirits. The two types are mentioned in the Book of the Prophet Jeremiah; "Circumcise yourselves to the Lord, and take away the foreskins of your heart" (4:4)

When he found that the morals of the Jewish people had been corrupted, Jeremiah stood up to address them, exhorting them to hold to upright morals, to make their intentions good and to avoid hypocrisy and lying, and telling them that the rabbis and Prophets could not remove corruption from the common people. That is why they needed to purify their morals and to circumcise their spirits as they circumcised their bodies. He also said: "Behold, the days come, saith the Lord, that I will punish all them which are circumcised with the uncircumcised; Egypt, and Judah, and Edom, and the children of Ammon, and Moab, and all that are in the utmost corners, that dwell in the wilderness; for all these nations are uncircumcised, and all the house of Israel are uncircumcised in the heart." (9:25-26)

After this brief mention of the two types of circumcision we should review some of what has been said about the origins of circumcision. What we find is scholars, ancient and modern, disagree about the origins of circumcision and when it was first practised.

According to the Gospel of Barnabas: "Then said Jesus: 'Adam the first man having eaten, by fraud of Satan, the food forbidden of

God in Paradise, his flesh rebelled against the spirit; whereupon he swore, saying, 'By God, I will cut thee!' And having broken a piece of rock, he seized his flesh to cut it with the sharp edge of the stone: whereupon he was rebuked by the angel Gabriel. And he answered: 'I have sworn by God to cut it; I will never be a liar!'

"Then the angel showed him the superfluity of his flesh and he cut that off. And hence, just as every man taketh flesh from the flesh of Adam, so is he bound to observe all that Adam promised with an oath. This did Adam observe in his sons, and from generation to generation came down the obligation of circumcision. But in the time of Abraham there were but few circumcised upon the earth, because that idolatry was multiplied upon the earth. Whereupon God told to Abraham the fact concerning circumcision, and made this covenant, saying: 'The soul that shall not have his flesh circumcised, I will scatter him among my people for ever.'" (23)

Shaykh 'Abdu'l-Wahhab al-Najjar says in his valuable book, *Stories of the Prophets*, "The Gospel of Barnabas states that the reason for circumcision was that when Adam disobeyed his Lord, he vowed to cut off a part of himself if Allah turned to him. When Allah accepted his repentance and Adam wanted to fulfil his vow, he was unsure about what to do and Jibril indicated this part and he cut it. Perhaps his descendants abandoned this *sunna* until Allah commanded Ibrahim to revive it."

According to Dr. Jawwad 'Ali, "The origin of circumcision was that it was one of the categories of blood sacrifice which man offered to his gods and it was considered a most important part of worship in ancient religions."

Some claim that circumcision began when ancient man first fashioned knives from flint. Iron knives were known in the 11th century BC and circumcision was known before this date.

The Torah states that circumcision has been practised since the covenant of Abraham; but this position is rejected by many scholars, who maintain that there is firm evidence dating from before the covenant of Ibrahim which indicates that many peoples used to practise circumcision. Similarly, there has been much research into the ancient covenant. Its critics affirm that it is unreliable because

11

many things crept in at the hands of the many transcribers and transmitters who were responsible for passing it on during the long period which passed between Musa and the earlier recording of the ancient covenant. Some researchers think that it occurred in the seventh or the fifth century BC.

There is another opinion which disagrees with what is found in the Torah and holds that circumcision became widespread from the time of Musa and that it originated in the house of Shu'ayb in the land of Midian. Another group reported that Isma'il was circumcised when he was thirteen.

Some books on pre-Islamic Arab history mention that the Ethiopians practised circumcision, as did the people of Australia and some North African tribes. As for the Egyptians, there is much evidence that they practised circumcision before the Jews did and there are monuments and engravings which show it. Some of these engravings date from the time of Amen-en-heb in the 15th cent BC. That is supported by the Greek historian Herodotus who states that "The ancient Egyptians used to circumcise themselves and many people adopted the idea of circumcision from them."

Muhammad 'Ashur says in his book *Circumcision in Divine and Man-made Laws:* "Circumcision among the ancient Egyptians was a requirement for anyone who was going to be a priest and enter the sacred place of worship, because circumcision was one of the hygienic necessities required for the cleanliness of all parts of the body since circumcision is cleansing of the sexual organs."

Circumcision is also mentioned in the Book of Leviticus in the context of discussing health and encouraging specific legislation for the treatment of sexual diseases such as segregating the sick. They took this so far that they burned the house in which the illness originated when the situation necessitated that. Moreover it appears that they did not acknowledge any wound as healthy other than that of circumcision.

So its prevalence as a religious practice among the ancient Egyptians and the Semites was not merely as a religious sacrifice to Allah but also as a hygienic measure against sexual disease, which perhaps explains why the Jews maintained it through their long wandering, diaspora and trials. The custom was transformed from a religious one to a matter of health.

Brifault tells us on this subject: "…This Jewish custom did not take the form it has today until a late period, namely in the time of the Maccabees (167 BC). At that time the procedure was done in a way which could be managed by Jewish mothers so that it would be done in such a manner that no one would know that it had been done. For that reason this the nationalist Jewish priests commanded that the foreskin be completely removed."

Is circumcision a distinguishing mark of the Jewish people?

Jewish people claim that circumcision is a distinguishing mark by which Allah has singled them out from all other people. As evidence of that they use texts from the Torah to justify their claim that circumcision is part of the covenant between God and themselves. Since much of what comes in the Torah is questionable we entertain some doubts about the exact nature of the covenant contracted between Allah and them in respect of circumcision. The Jewish people are not the only people to claim that there was a covenant between them and their Creator, and there are many peoples who adopted circumcision besides the Jews.

Muhammad 'Ashur says in *Circumcision in Divine and Manmade Laws*: "If Allah chose circumcision as a distinguishing mark for them unlike any other people, how do we explain the circumcision of other peoples before them such as the Egyptians, Australians and others? It seems that it existed at the time of Nuh, but that later among the Christians circumcision was transformed and took the form of baptism."

A few scholars, especially among the Jews, believe that the origin of the idea lies in the fact that it was a custom performed by someone who fled for sanctuary to a temple. He had to have a sign to protect him from his master or his enemies; this sign took several forms, of which circumcision was one and tattooing another.

Tattooing – making an indelible mark on the hand or another part of the body – has been practised since ancient times. It is considered as a sign which can make one man distinct from another by an image or writing imprinted on the body. Many nations and ancient peoples used tattooing, such as the Greeks, the Romans and the Graeco-Egyptians under the Ptolemies. According to various ancient sources, the Greeks and the Romans practised it and the Ptolemies utilised it to distinguish the Jews from the Egyptians, it being used for this purpose by Ptolemy VI. Another type of tattooing used by some people is to burn part of the ear lobe, which was perhaps the origin of women piercing their ears and wearing ear-rings.

All of this confirms that circumcision and similar things are not a specific characteristic of the Jewish people since it was performed by many peoples before and after the Jews. The fact that circumcision is mentioned in the Torah cannot be taken as absolute proof, for the truth is the contrary. The Torah contains many changes and has been subject to much alteration and deviation which makes it unreliable and not acceptable as definitive evidence as to the truth or falsehood of anything.

The Time of Circumcision

There are many opinions about the whole business of circumcision. Scholars and *fuqaha'* disagree about whether it is obligatory or merely permissible. Those who consider it obligatory disagree as to the age at which it should be carried out. Almost all Jewish scholars – with the exception of a few sects – agree that circumcision is obligatory on the eighth day after birth. That accords with the text of the Torah (Genesis 17:10-14) and the Talmud (Seth 19:1):

"This is my covenant, which ye shall keep, between me and you and thy seed after thee; every man child among you shall be circumcised. And ye shall circumcise the flesh of your foreskin; and it shall be a token of the covenant betwixt me and you. And he that is eight days old shall be circumcised among you, every man child in your generations, he that is born in the house, or bought with money of any stranger, which is not of thy seed. And the uncircumcised man child whose flesh of his foreskin is not circumcised, that soul shall be cut off from his people; he hath broken my covenant."

On the basis of this text, the Jews believe that the time for circumcision is the eighth day after the male child is born and it is not permissible to delay it, whatever the circumstances. With modern developments, however, some alterations have entered into the time defined for circumcision in Jewish Law, some Jewish groups now opposing that rule regarding the time of circumcision.

For instance, we find that the group of Samaritans and the Karaites say that if the child is ill or his health would be impaired by circumcision it is possible to delay the operation. The father may choose the appropriate time for the child according to his state of health. Similarly, according to the *Beth Din*, the Jewish Legal Court, the health of the child should be taken into account when considering the proper time for circumcision.

Those who live to the south-west of the Arab lands specify certain days of the month on which circumcision is better than others. Those days are the 7th, 14th, 21st, and 28th. Some people in eastern Africa circumcise the child in the first or second month. The Persian Muslims differed completely and used to circumcise their children when their bodies grew stronger at the age of three. The Copts used to carry out the operation of circumcision in the third or sixth year, preferring to circumcise before the baptism of the child. The Fijians preferred the seventh year. Some tribes preferred to circumcise at puberty.

The result of this is that the disagreement about the right time to carry out circumcision has been the subject of debate in world conferences with the object of reaching a proper opinion based on the knowledge of the leading specialists to protect the best health interests of the child.

One specialist, Dr. al-Barbari, says on this subject: "There is no doubt that carrying out circumcision immediately after birth represents a danger to the life of the child, since it is known that the substances necessary for clotting the blood begin to form in the intestines of the breast-feeding child after about six days and their formation is complete after a maximum of fifteen days. Thus children who have the procedure performed one or two days after birth are exposed to the possibility of severe haemorrhage which may threaten their lives." For this reason Dr al-Barbari advised that the procedure should take place on the fourteenth day after the birth of the child.

According to this the foreskin, which is completely removed in circumcision, should only be cut off after the fifteenth day and, despite its simplicity, circumcision is for this reason considered a dangerous procedure if it takes place before the child is two weeks old. When it is absolutely imperative for circumcision to be carried out on the first or second day – if, for instance, a child is unable to urinate – then the procedure must be carried out early and the child should be given vitamin K a day before the procedure to guard against the danger of haemorrhage.

Dr. al-Barbari also holds that the time of the operation should not be delayed beyond the first three months of the child's life. That is because the child's sensation and perception begin from three months and the injury will also heal very quickly at that young age.

The Importance of the Circumcision Gathering

It is customary for every family to hold a gathering for the circumcision of their children. Such parties take different forms according to religions, customs and traditions but are always occasions of joy. As we have seen, among Jews circumcision takes place on the eighth day after birth and a party is held after it, which no fewer than ten males should attend. This number is called 'minyan'. In the celebration the father thanks God and thanks those who are present, praying that the child will grow and marry and have a good future. Those present then drink a special type of wine. Then he announces the name of the child and puts a few drops on his lips before sending a cup of some of the wine to the child's mother, since she does not attend the party with the men.

The Sephardic Jews recite Psalm 128; those present at the circumcision must stand and not sit, in accordance with II Kings 2:13. There is an empty chair on which no one is allowed to sit in the room in which the circumcision gathering is held. It is called the chair of the Prophet Elijah. The child is carried by a man called the *sandek*, who sits on a chair next to the chair of the Prophet Elijah. Then those present read some verses from the Torah such as Genesis 49:18, and Psalms 119 and 65 and they also read something about Elijah.

The chair of the Prophet Elijah is the subject of a legend. The Jews claim that the Prophet Elijah appeared in the 9th century BC in Israel and began to admonish the people and the king, saying that they should embark on the path of reform and worship Allah and avoid worship of idols and false gods. But his advice was not heeded. The King of Israel at that time was Ahab ibn Omri. Ahab took a pagan wife: Jezebel, the daughter of Ethbaal King of Zidonians. At the time there was a famine as a result of five dry years in Israel and the Prophet Elijah said to them: "Where are your prophets, O you who worship idols? If your prophets are sent from God, then ask them to pray for rain." The King said, "We will gather our prophets and you attend, and then it will be known who is the real prophet: you or they."

At the gathering, the Prophet Elijah said to them, "Offer your sacrifices. If Allah accepts them, rain will fall. If He does not accept them, then rain will not fall." So they made their sacrifices, but they were not accepted and no rain fell. Then Elijah asked Allah to accept his sacrifice and to accept his supplication. His Lord answered him and the rain fell and watered the parched earth. King Ahab and his pagan wife Jezebel were at a loss, especially after Elijah slew the pagan prophets of Baal. Then the King and his wife drove out the Prophet Elijah and he had to flee from their aggression to another land until Allah took him back. The details of this are recounted in I Kings 18.

The Jews believe that the Prophet Elijah will descend to earth again and that he attends the circumcision gathering of every Jewish child without anyone seeing him. This belief is the reason for leaving a chair empty which is called Elijah's Chair: so that the Prophet may descend to this gathering and find his chair empty and sit on it.

The General Reasons for Circumcision

There are a number of reasons given for circumcision, which we will examine here.

* **Distinguishing Mark**

    Some tribes considered circumcision a distinguishing mark for their sons, as was shown in times of wars and captives. This was the case, for instance, in the Battle of Hunayn between the Muslims and idolaters at the time of the Prophet Muhammad, may Allah bless him and grant him peace, since the Christian Arabs were not circumcised. That is what also occurred in the wars between the Jews and the Romans. The idea was prevalent among Bedouin tribes that circumcision was a sign which marked out a person belonging to a particular tribe.

* **Scientific**

    Some scholars think that circumcision was a type of sacrifice which man offered to his Lord, especially out of the desire for fertility. This belief was prevalent among certain South American tribes. At times in their history, the Jews also considered circumcision a type of sacrifice and an offering from man to his Lord.

- **Hygienic**

  The ancient Egyptians practised circumcision for hygienic reasons. Some scholars say that some tribes in hot lands practise circumcision without consciously considering the health aspect; but the truth is that it originated from health reasons.

- **Erotic**

  Some consider circumcision a factor in prolonging male sexual pleasure.

- **Surrogate Sacrifice**

  Circumcision is a surrogate form of human sacrifice in that part of the body is sacrificed in place of the entire body.

- **Class Differentiation**

  Circumcision was used as distinguishing mark between classes of people as, for example, in the case of the circumcision of priests in ancient Egypt. The same applies to the priests of Babylon, who were circumcised while other groups in that society were not.

- **Tribal Marking**

  The laws and customs of some tribes demanded that those who joined them should be circumcised. Only after circumcision did one become a member of that society. That is the case with the Jews. If someone wants to embrace Judaism, he must be circumcised unless he already is.

- **Purification**

  Circumcision is a type of purification. The Muslims call this operation *tahara* or *tahur,* which means purity. This indicates that for Muslims circumcision is a form of purification and connected with cleanliness, cleanliness being part of faith.

- **Custom**

  In some places circumcision is simply a tradition which people hold to and keep as a popular custom. Some people forbid marriage with an uncircumcised person. In such places custom demands that people be circumcised if they want to propose to a girl.

- **Religious ritual**

  Circumcision is sometimes considered a religious ritual, and that is the slant which Jews tend to give to it.

Perhaps the reason that Jewish people in particular give circumcision a religious slant is because it is considered part of the covenant between God and themselves, as is related in Genesis and also in Joshua 5:7-9: "And their children, whom he raised up in their stead, them Joshua circumcised; for they were uncircumcised, because they had not circumcised them by the way. And it came to pass, when they had done circumcising all the people, that they abode in their places in the camp, till they were whole. And the Lord said unto Joshua, This day I have rolled away the reproach of Egypt from off you. Wherefore the name of the place is called Gilgal unto this day."

Some scholars think that religion has played a major part in circumcision for a long time as it has played a large role in human life as a whole. That would make religion one of the main causes of circumcision. According to Muhammad 'Ashur, the religious element in circumcision was not confined to the Jews, but also formed part of the religious practice of other peoples. As for circumcision being a pact between God and the people, Nuh came before the Jews and there was also a covenant between him and Allah.

In favour of the claim that circumcision is a national and religious sign, we find in the *Encyclopaedia of Zionist Concepts and Terms* by Dr 'Abdu'l-Wahhab al-Masiri: "If a child dies before the seventh day his body is circumcised and he is given a Hebrew name so as to obtain a Jewish identity. That eliminates any hygienic or generally human motive for circumcision and proves it to be purely an ethnic religious sign."

The connection between circumcision and sacrifice

Some scholars believe circumcision to be a surrogate human sacrifice – in other words, a major human sacrifice which diminished until it took the form of circumcision. According to this view sacrifice is the basis of circumcision. It stemmed from human sacrifice in ancient times when people would sacrifice some of their children when an important problem had to be dealt with. The Phoenicians participated in such barbaric rites. Fathers would come to the gathering dressed in their finery as at a festival and the drums were beaten and flutes played to drown out the screams of their children who were being burnt on the altars of the gods! Gradually, however, this savage act became mitigated and the priests would beat themselves so that their own blood splashed on the altar; or they would sacrifice an animal in place of the child, or cut off the child's foreskin, to propitiate their gods.

There is no religion which does not have some form of sacrifice. It is found in the religions of pagans, Magians, Zoroastrians, Manichaeans, Sabians, totemists, star worshippers, animal and plant worshippers as well as in the laws of the Jews, Christians and Muslims. In pagan religions circumcision was sometimes performed as a sacrifice to the god of fertility and procreation, and a part of the human body was cut to propitiate that deity.

Muhammad 'Ashur discusses this topic in his book *Circumcision in Divine and Man-made Laws*. He says:

> Scholars disagree about circumcision, especially Jewish scholars. While some of them consider it a type of sacrifice, others do not think of it in that way. We find that scholars who consider it a type of sacrifice say that there is a resemblance between circumcision and burnt sacrifices, as in the Jewish religion, since in burnt sacrifices in the Jewish religion only part of the sacrificed animal must be offered in this way under the supervision of the Levite

priest. In both cases – burnt sacrifices and circumcision – a part represents the whole in performing the ritual.

There is another resemblance between circumcision and sacrifice, blood is spilt in both cases, and this precondition coincides with the Jewish idea which says that "God delights in spilt blood and that which bespatters the wall of the temple."

In any event, it seems clear from this that Jewish Law ordains circumcision as a religious rite – although opponents of this view put forward the following points to support their conclusion.

- Circumcision does not have to be done by a priest. It can be done by any doctor.
- Circumcision is performed not in the synagogue but at home or in a hospital.
- The blood shed from circumcision is not sprinkled on the wall of the synagogue as mentioned in the texts of the Torah.

The Jews holding to male circumcision despite persecution

According to Muhammad 'Ashur, "The Jews continued to practice male circumcision on their children and did not give up this religious symbol even in the most difficult periods of their history, such as those in which they suffered from a great deal of persecution."

For example, they continued to practice circumcision while they were in Babylon in the days of the Babylonian Captivity (from 586 BC until about 444 BC), because they believed that circumcision was one of the signs which distinguished them from other peoples and so they always tried to practise it, no matter what punishments were inflicted on them.

For that reason they were exposed to many hardships and difficulties because they clung to this religious custom. Although they were subjected to torture by the ruling authorities during the time of the Romans and the injustice of the inquisition, nevertheless they would not renounce the practice.

At one time they even used to circumcise themselves, because the Roman authorities made execution the penalty for those who performed circumcision, whether it was the mother or anyone else. Antiochus Epiphanes prohibited it for the Jews and that provoked the Maccabee rebellion in 165 BC, when the Jews revolted against the Roman authorities.

When Hadrian became the Roman Emperor, he issued an edict forbidding the Jews to circumcise their children and that edict led to war between the Jews and Romans under the Jewish leader Bar Kochba. This war ended in a Jewish defeat but they still continued to maintain the practice of circumcision and other Jewish rituals. Eventually Philo, the Jewish philosopher, declared that this custom had many hygienic benefits. He made a heroic defence of his Jewish brethren because of their holding to this custom.

The result of the strong adherence to this custom on the part of the Jews and their philosopher was that there were some Roman emperors who thought it best not to become embroiled in this custom and the Emperor Antonius allowed the Jews the freedom to practise circumcision.

The Christians and circumcision

It is known from a reading of ancient history that Jesus, peace be upon him, was circumcised at the age of eight days. The Jewish Law continued to be followed by Christians until Paul unilaterally disclaimed what the Jewish faith holds about circumcision. We find that Paul allowed Christians to dispense with circumcision and removed this imposition from them. He says in the First Epistle to Corinthians (7:18-19): "Is any man called being circumcised? let him not become uncircumcised. Is any called in uncircumcision? let him not be circumcised. Circumcision is nothing, and uncircumcision is nothing, but the keeping of the commandments of God."

We find the same kind of thing in the Epistle to the Ephesians (2:11-13): "Wherefore remember, that ye being in time past Gentiles in the flesh, who are called Uncircumcision by that which is called the circumcision in the flesh made by hands; that at that time ye were without Christ, being aliens from the commonwealth of Israel, and strangers from the covenants of promise, having no hope, and without God in the world; but now in Christ Jesus ye who sometimes were far off are made nigh by the blood of Christ."

The Christians disagree as to whether circumcision is compulsory or voluntary. Some – and those are the Christians with Jewish roots who embraced Christianity – say that it is compulsory. Others hold that circumcision is not compulsory in view of what the Council of Jerusalem decided on the subject: "Circumcision is not compulsory in Christianity. This is how Christians proceed. The Copts in Egypt, however, prefer the custom of circumcision which has been prevalent in Egypt since the time of the Pharaohs, and because the Copts are the Christians of Egypt and have this custom."

The dispute between the Jews and the Christians concerning circumcision

Jesus, peace be upon him, was born a Jew and grew up and completed his duty to Allah by delivering the Message he had been charged with, never repudiating the basic tenets of Mosaic law. This proved to be a bone of contention among his followers after he left them. Most of them continued in his footsteps but some, Paul in particular, abandoned Jewish law for mainly popularist reasons. Circumcision was one of the topics on which there was some controversy.

In the debate which took place between Paul and some of the Jews, the Jews said, "Except ye be circumcised after the manner of Moses, ye cannot be saved." (Acts 15:1) Paul replied, "And God, who knoweth the hearts, bare them witness, giving them the Holy Ghost, even as he did unto us; and put no difference between us and them, purifying their hearts by faith." (Acts 15:8-9)

This is an example of the kind of argument he used: "For circumcision verily profiteth, if thou keep the law; but if thou be a breaker of the law, thy circumcision is made uncircumcision. Therefore if the uncircumcised keep the righteousness of the law, shall not his uncircumcision be counted for circumcision? And shall not uncircumcision which is by nature, if it fulfil the law, judge thee, who by the letter and circumcision dost transgress the law? But he is a Jew, which is one inwardly; and circumcision is that of the heart, in the spirit, and not in the letter; whose praise is not of men, but of God." (Romans 2:25-29)

The important thing to bear in mind here is that there is no real Divine or Prophetic justification for this position taken by Paul whereby he jettisoned the law of Moses to the great consternation of most of the other followers of Jesus.

Circumcision among the Arabs

Even before the dawn of Islam there were Arabs who held to circumcision, although those who embraced Christianity did not hold to it, because of the Pauline position.

In the books of *Sira* we find that when the Ansar finished off the slain of the tribe of Thaqif who fell in the battle of Hunayn against Hawazin they found a slave. When they came to despoil him, they found he was uncircumcised. When that was clear to the Ansar, one of them called out in a loud voice: "Allah knows that Thaqif is uncircumcised."

Al-Mughira ibn Shu'ba, who belonged to Thaqif, went and took his hand, fearing that that would be believed about his people among the Arabs, and said, "Do not say that. May my father and mother be your ransom, it is a Christian slave. Then he began to expose the dead of his people for the man who had shouted out and he agreed, "We see that they are circumcised."

According to Dr. Jawwad 'Ali, "Circumcision was considered one of the customs of the ancient *Jahiliyya* and in that respect the Arabs were like the Hebrews. It is a matter which the Qur'an does not mention but it is mentioned in *hadith*."

There is a report in which the historian Josephus says: "The Arabs used to circumcise their children at the age of ten," although it must be said that from a survey of the most of the history books about the Arabs in the *Jahiliyya* it is clear that the Arabs did not have a definite tradition of circumcision. The author of *Details of the History of the Arabs before Islam* mentioned that the Romans forbade the Arabs to circumcise – which would suggest that it certainly took place.

Abu'l-Fida' reports that "Circumcision was practised by the pagans in the land of the Arabs." The Arabs used to have circumcision gatherings, especially when the child passed from childhood to manhood and maturity, and after circumcision the child became a responsible man. There were some ancient customs in these gatherings: the child wore certain garments and had a tarboosh on his head embroidered with gold thread.

The Arabs used to regard circumcision as a commendable form of cleanliness and they described as *'hanifs'* those who followed the religion of Ibrahim. It was called 'the Greatest Religion'. The meaning of *'hanif'* is 'pure' because they were circumcised, avoided foul things, and affirmed the unity of Allah. The Arabs called anyone who went on *hajj* or circumcised himself a *hanif*. He was considered as following the religion of Ibrahim the Friend, peace be upon him.

Female Circumcision

We have discussed the subject of male circumcision and its origins in Divine and man-made systems. We described the Jewish religious position in some detail since there are many innovations and much misguidance among them regarding this complex topic which is the result of the great number of changes and alterations that have been introduced into the Torah.

An additional difficulty in the topic, which is more important, compels us to examine the position of various religions regarding female circumcision and arrive at a definitive position on this matter through an examination of the position of the Islamic *Shari'a* as propounded by the great reliable *fuqaha'* of this time, supported by clear evidence while at the same time taking into account the view of medical science.

Before we deal with the opinions of religion and science about female circumcision in the Islamic *Shari'a,* we will first examine the opinion of Jewish scholars and Christian scholars, beginning with the Jewish position.

The position of the Jewish religion regarding female circumcision

There does not appear to be any text or even a reference to female circumcision anywhere in the Torah; all we find is the call for the Jewish people to circumcise their boys. For instance, we read the following text in Genesis: "And Abraham circumcised his son Isaac being eight days old, as God had commanded him." (Genesis 21:4). We also find in Leviticus 12:3: "And in the eighth day the flesh of his foreskin shall be circumcised." Also in Exodus 12:48: "And when a stranger shall sojourn with thee, and will keep the passover to the Lord, let all his males be circumcised."

Indeed Jewish Law forbids female circumcision according to what is stated in their books. According to the *Book of Jewish Festivals and Customs*, "There is no circumcision for girls. The girl is taken with her mother about a month after the period of post-natal bleeding to the synagogue and the cantor recites some verses and then calls the girl by the name which her mother has chosen for her."

The position of the Christian and other cultures regarding female circumcision

Christian law does not say anything about female circumcision. Mary As'ad, a researcher in the Centre for Social Studies, says: "Female circumcision is not part of Christianity or Judaism as religions." There is also the research of Dr. Ghalioungui which it maintains that female circumcision is an ancient African and Pharaonic custom.

Regarding the Egyptian people, the traveller Strabo says that Egyptian women were circumcised, although female circumcision did not take the form of excision and infibulation. The scholar Erman says, "As for male and female circumcision, the preferred time for doing it was the time when the Nile floods."

In some places in India female circumcision is performed for special purposes, such as lessening sexual desire and limiting the amount of copulation. There are other regions, like Baluchistan, where female circumcision is performed at the time of the wedding.

After this brief review of female and male circumcision in divine and man-made systems, we will move to the definitive position, which is the view of the Islamic *Shari'a* in detail, accompanied by medical opinions.

Part II
Two Medical Opinions
regarding Circumcision

Female Circumcision
in Medicine and Islam

Dr. Hamid al-Ghawabi in *Liwa' al-Islam*
(A supporter of female circumcision)

Some magazines have dealt with this problem many times. The attack on female circumcision began when the magazine *ad-Duktur* published a supplement to its issue of May 1951 devoted to female circumcision in which some doctors who thought that there was no harm in it gave their opinions and others maintained that there was grave psychological and social harm in it.

Some of them actually opposed Islam, contending that no doctor should allow it and that there is nothing in the Prophetic *hadiths* or in the reports of the imams which indicate female circumcision whereas there clearly is about male circumcision. That is why I think it is incumbent on me to clarify the position of Islam concerning this matter and then to follow it with my personal medical opinion.

The Prophet, may Allah bless him and grant him peace, said "Circumcision is a *sunna* for men and an honourable deed for women." Is there anything better than this honourable deed which – as I will make clear – limits desire and lessens arousal while at the same time not depriving women of sexual pleasure?

Look at what the Messenger said when the women emigrated and among them was a woman called Umm Habiba. She used to circumcise girls. When the Messenger of Allah, may Allah bless him and grant him peace, saw her, he asked her, "Umm Habiba, are you still practising today what you used to practise before?" She said, "Yes, Messenger of Allah, unless it is forbidden and you forbid me to do it." He said, "It is allowed. Come closer so that I can teach you." She went closer to him and he said, "Umm

Habiba, if you do it, do not overdo it because it brings more radiance to the face and it is more pleasant for the husband."

Notice the words, "Do not overdo it," meaning "Do not remove the clitoris entirely." Medicine had not shown anything about this sensitive part, the clitoris, or cutting the nerves in it, but the Messenger, may Allah bless him and grant him peace who was instructed by the All-Aware, All-Knowing knew that and ordered that this part should not be completely excised.

If the operation of circumcision is done correctly, medically speaking, the clitoris is not excised completely. Only part of it is cut: the epidermis and the end of the clitoris. This tip is extremely sensitive. There is also sensitivity in the part which remains but it is somewhat reduced.

The doctors who wrote in the magazine said that circumcision completely deprives the woman of sexual pleasure; but the truth is that a girl who is circumcised merely has less sexual desire than those who have not been circumcised. In their case any contact with the clitoris, even from their clothes, can produce intense sexual arousal. Where married women are concerned, feeling remains in it but their libido is not excessive and so they are self-possessed and self-controlled rather than wanton. So sexual arousal is not absent from circumcised women: it is merely reduced to a level which is not harmful.

I believe that female circumcision has the following medical benefits:

- There are discharges from the labia minora. If these labia are not excised with part of the clitoris in circumcision, the discharges can collect, turn rancid and give off an unpleasant smell and inflammations can result which can extend to the vagina and even to the urinary passage. I have see many cases of such inflammation in women because of lack of circumcision.

- Such circumcision lessens the sensitivity of the girl so that sexual arousal does not occur from mere contact and the girl does not become neurotic from youth.

31

The Messenger of Allah, may Allah bless him and grant him peace, said, "Circumcision is an honourable deed for women and it brings more radiance to the face," when the clitoris is not completely removed. If it is the woman will have a neurotic nature and a yellowish colouring. But we think that circumcision must be carried out by doctors and trained practitioners and not left to ignorant women.

I read a refutation of my article, "Female Circumcision in Medicine and Islam" in the magazine *Liwa' al-Islam* in which the author says: "I was astonished to read the article by a colleague in the magazine calling for female circumcision!"

He said that in my article I relied on the *hadith* of the Messenger of Allah, may Allah bless him and grant him peace, with Umm Habiba who used to perform circumcision on girls, and that the Messenger met her after she emigrated and asked, "Umm Habiba, are you still practising today what you used to practise before?" meaning, "Are you performing female circumcision in Madina as you did in Makka?" She replied, "Yes, Messenger of Allah, unless it is forbidden and you forbid me to do it." He said: "Umm Habiba, if you cut, do not overdo it because that brings more radiance to the face and it is more pleasant for the husband." My colleague adds: "Even if this *hadith* is sound without any defect, we do not think that it shows that the Messenger confirmed Umm Habiba in her action. Rather it indicates that he disapproved of it but used this opportunity to alter her procedure if she had to carry it out.

I reply to my colleague that the Messenger, may Allah bless him and grant him peace, did not speak from whim. If he was not supporting Umm Habiba in her action but in fact objected to it, why did he not forbid her to do it and tell her not to circumcise girls? She asked him, may Allah bless him and grant him peace, if he forbade her and if it was *haram*. If the Messenger had not wished it, he would have prohibited it instead of teaching her the method of sound circumcision, telling her not to overdo it.

The Messenger, may Allah bless him and grant him peace, did prohibit several things on medical grounds. He said, "Do not urinate in standing water and then perform *wudu'* with it," to guard against illnesses like bilharzia and other water-borne diseases. He also forbade marriage with close relatives, saying, "Do not marry close relatives. The child may be malformed," a principle corroborated by medical science after his lifetime. He said, "Select for your sperm and do not waste it on those who are not your equals." This was an early example of genetic science which modern science has confirmed many centuries later. There are other medical Prophetic *hadiths* in which the Prophet forbade certain actions.

In the previous *hadith* about circumcision, when the Prophet, may Allah bless him and grant him peace, saw a woman who carried it out using a procedure involving radical excision, which entails actual harm, he told her, "Do not overdo it," meaning "Do not cut too much." That was in order to protect girls and to preserve a degree of sensitivity for them. If it is excessive it is harmful and if it is totally lacking it is harmful.

It must be remembered that the Messenger, may Allah bless him and grant him peace, was receiving Revelation from his Lord and that his Lord was teaching him knowledge directly from Him, so he would have realised that circumcision was harmful and would have clearly forbidden it. His words, "if you do it" mean "if you continue to do this action and do not change it for another work." "Do not overdo it" is a clear prohibition in which there is no doubt or uncertainty.

Regarding the unpleasant smell which comes from the fluid trapped within the vagina, there is no remedy for it but ablation of the labia minora. Otherwise however much a woman washes herself a trace of this smell always remains.

Some of my colleagues says that female circumcision causes sexual frigidity which leads some wives to use drugs and hashish. Female circumcision of the kind we see carried out by some midwives who excise the entire clitoris may indeed lead to sexual frigidity; but this is not the circumcision which the Messenger of Allah indicated. Correct circumcision has been performed on a huge number of girls and most of them have married without suffering from sexual frigidity. There are many causes of sexual frigidity which are not connected with this problem and which we will mention. The point is that we do not advocate complete excision in female circumcision but follow the *hadith* of the Messenger, "Do not overdo it."

The same colleague wonders at my statement that the parts which are cut in circumcision are sensitive to the degree that their contact with clothes provokes arousal, and says that this is silly and far from true. But he himself says that the clitoris is sensitive and erective. If this member which is upright is rubbed by anything, it increases its sensitivity.

Then he mentions that the hormones of the woman start to flag after the age of thirty. I reply that this is one of the religious and medical benefits of circumcision because a man is frequently considerably older than his wife. If the difference between them is ten, fifteen, twenty years or more as is sometimes the case, what happens when a husband is fifty or more and his energy flags and his vitality weakens while his wife is still under thirty and in her sexual prime?

How could such a man preserve his health if he found before him a woman who still retained the full force of her youth and an undiminished sexual drive when his had lessened? Clearly in this case a man is forced to overextend himself or leave his wife unsatisfied, neither of which is advisable. But when the woman has had a partial circumcision, her sexual appetite is reasonable and the husband and wife are in a comparable state.

There are medical cases of a condition known as nymphomania which is when women have excessive sexual desire. The sexual appetite of such women is so strong that their husbands are made ill by their demands and, indeed, in extreme cases it can cause their death. This is far less frequent among circumcised women.

Muslims should know that we do not call for female circumcision in the excessive manner in which some ignorant women carry it out, but we call for their circumcision in the balanced way to which the greatest doctor of all, the Messenger of Allah, may Allah bless him and grant him peace, guided us. No one should try to change the *hadiths* of the Messenger of Allah according to his own whims. The noble Messenger did not speak from whim at all. He was guided by Allah in every instance.

As we have seen, the main argument of the medical opponents of female circumcision is that excision of the clitoris leads to frigidity in women. There is accepted evidence, however, that this is not the case. Professor Huhner, professor of gynaecology in the University of New York in America, who is the author of many papers on this subject published in many countries, said in his book, *Sexual Diseases*: last edition, p. 391: "The tears resulting from childbirth which cause a widening in the opening of the vagina, are a factor in inducing sexual frigidity in women which is the opposite of what might be expected. On the other hand, injuries to the clitoris and the illnesses which affect it rarely lead to sexual frigidity."

He also says that in cases where clitoris is not fully developed – or not present at all – when it is affected by some unusual illness, or when it is completely paralysed with no feeling whatsoever, it rarely affects the desire of the woman for sexual relations or causes sexual frigidity. That being the case, how do these doctors deduce that cutting part of the clitoris leads to sexual frigidity? Where is their evidence?

In fact the Messenger of Allah, indicated the treatment which truly prevents sexual frigidity when he advised his companions to send a message to their wives before having sexual intercourse with them. When they asked him what he meant, he said, "A kiss or something like that." This indicates that it is foreplay before sexual intercourse which is one of the greatest means of preventing sexual frigidity. He said, may Allah bless him and grant him peace, "It is unacceptable for a man to go to his slavegirl or wife and have intercourse with her before speaking to her and being friendly with her." The Messenger of Allah is our guide in everything. He never spoke from whim and he was the greatest teacher of people in all affairs, even in these very intimate matters.

The true causes of sexual frigidity and lack of sexual satisfaction in women, some of which are mentioned here, have nothing to do with partial excision of the clitoris. They include:

- Incompatibility between the sexual organs of the husband and wife, such as when the vagina of the woman is wide because of childbirth or the man's penis too small, or vice versa.

- Tears in the woman's sexual parts following childbirth.

- Flaccidity of the penis.

- Premature ejaculation.

- Coitus interruptus.

- Swollen skin.

- Psychological reasons, such as lack of love between the couple, the woman's fear of becoming pregnant, or resulting from faulty teachings about sex.

These are the reasons given by medical books as the reasons for sexual frigidity. Cutting the clitoris in circumcision is not among them.

Circumcision of Children in Medicine and Islam

Dr. Muhammad Sa'id al-Hadidi
(An opponent of female circumcision)

Dr. Muhammad Sa'id al-Hadidi gave an excellent lecture on the verses concerned with medicine in the Holy Qur'an and the opinion of science and medicine regarding circumcision, mentioning its history and its effects from a psychological, social and moral point of view in the life of individual men and women and its effects in the life of the community as a whole. He spoke in some detail about male circumcision.

The circumcision procedure in men involves completely removing the foreskin, which is the thin piece of skin which covers the glans of the penis and the opening of the urinary canal. It contains no arteries or large veins, having only fine capillary vessels which do not cause excessive bleeding unless the procedure is carried out improperly and the penis itself cut into.

The male organ has two functions: urination and procreation. Removal of the foreskin, which encircles the frontal opening of the urinary canal, has many benefits some of which I will mention here:

- Sometimes the opening of the foreskin is very narrow or even non-existent. This medical condition, known as strangulation, results in intense pain followed by swelling and retention of urine and ending in uraemia which is life-threatening. This condition is sometimes found in newborn male babies and its remedial treatment is immediate circumcision.

- Some droplets of urine may be trapped by the foreskin and under it around the glans, which can result in inflammation at the end of the penis and the foreskin. The best treatment is circumcision. We often see men who need this procedure later in life.

- Lack of circumcision and possible consequential inflammation of the male organ and foreskin may result in a dangerous illness known as cancer of the penis. This illness is rarely helped by any treatment except complete removal of the entire penis and often leads to the person becoming an invalid permanently.

- There are also other illnesses which may develop owing to lack of circumcision and which affect the urinary tract and procreative organs, such as sepsis and other disorders.

This explains some of the medical benefits of male circumcision and so we can see that there is wisdom in it. Male circumcision has been known from ancient times and in many religions.

The circumcision procedure for women

The procedure of circumcision for women is completely different from that of men from every point of view – anatomical, surgical and physiological, as well as psychological and social – and I will try to show here the devastating effect it can have.

As practised in Egypt, female circumcision does not only remove a small piece of flesh analogous to the foreskin of the man, but completely removes the clitoris and the labia minora. What is intended by this complete excision is to deprive the woman of this organ which Allah gave her to experience sexual pleasure in order to curb her sexual desire.

Just as I earlier explained the benefits of male circumcision, I will here present the harmful effects which stem from this operation when it is performed on women. I say "harmful effects" because I do not know of a single benefit resulting from it.

Female circumcision frequently results in severe haemorrhaging because, as I explained, this procedure excises the entire clitoris which contains important blood vessels. I will confine myself to what was said by the Dean of Medicine, 'Ali Ibrahim, in a lecture he gave on Tuesday, 18 December 1928 in the General Medical Convention which was held in Cairo in that year:

> "In all cases (speaking of female circumcision) important blood vessels are cut and in some cases that results in severe haemorrhage. Frankly, I can tell you that all my information about his procedure (female circumcision) comes from the numerous cases to which I have been summoned to stop a severe haemorrhage resulting from it."

That is the surgical result of female circumcision but it is not in itself crucial since it can be easily overcome when the procedure is carried out using sound surgical techniques. This is what should be followed in the very rare cases when female circumcision must be performed, as I will explain, so it is a danger which can be countered. But there is another harmful effect which damages women both psychologically and socially.

Circumcision as usually practised on women is in some ways comparable to having the tongue cut out. With no tongue we would no longer be able to taste and enjoy the food we eat. Similarly a circumcised wife who has had her organ of sexual sensitivity removed in its entirety is unable to experience any sexual feeling and this tends to make the sexual act hard and difficult. We see this in all circumcised women and find that they need to compensate in other ways for the loss of sexual sensitivity which prevents them experiencing sexual pleasure.

Circumcision in men is a hygienic precaution which aims at keeping the glans of the penis clean – but what is the wisdom in the circumcision of girls? Why deprive a woman of her clitoris, which is intended for sexual pleasure, and what effect does that deprival have on her psychology? The psychological effect on the woman and her nervous state is clear and evident in the damage and irregularities which we observe in the Egyptian family, high and low, rich and poor, educated and uneducated.

A woman who lacks most of her sexual sensitivity and finds it difficult to enjoy the sexual act tends to suffer from hidden psychological disturbance and the sharpness in her nature and her neurosis increases. It is impossible to calm her agitation and bitterness and she is never satisfied. This inner agitation increases to such an extent that it has harmful effects on the family, and the homes of such hard, dry women become the source of significant social and psychological problems.

But the harm of female circumcision goes beyond this, one surprising directly related problem being the spread of drugs and narcotics of all types. It has been shown that there has been a significant increase in the consumption of these substances by men who desire to increase their sexual endurance in order to try to give sexual satisfaction to their circumcised wives.

Undoubtedly many have considered this question and some believe female circumcision to be a means of curbing women's sexual desire to a large extent. There are those who consider this to be an adequate benefit, however numerous its concomitant harmful effects, if it truly protects their reputation and maintains their chastity and honour. Anyone who believes this is mistaken.

The basis and existence of sexual desire in men and women is the same. It arises from endocrines secreted by the testicles and ovaries. The ovaries are in the woman's abdominal cavity and there is no way for anyone who wants to kill this natural desire in her to reach them. Hence it is evident to us that the basic sexual desire remains, and this desire varies in every individual, male or female, according to their nature. The danger comes when the means of satisfying this desire are lacking. Circumcised women are in danger on one hand of taking extreme steps to satisfy their sexual appetite and on the other of becoming arid and embittered because they are unable to do so.

Circumcision in Islam

As regards the Islamic view of circumcision, the Noble Qur'an makes no mention whatsoever of this operation, whether in men or women. In the case of the Prophet, may Allah bless him and grant him peace, there are many *hadiths*. They can be divided into two categories: those relating to male circumcision, and those relating to female circumcision.

Abu Hurayra reported that the Messenger of Allah, may Allah bless him and grant him peace, said, "The natural way of man (*fitra*) involves five things: shaving the pubic hair, circumcision, trimming the moustache, removing hair from the armpits and cutting the nails". This is reported by al-Bukhari and Muslim. Scholars disagree about the *fitra*. According to Imam al-Khattabi some scholars say that it is the *Sunna*. Ibn Hajar says in the commentary on al-Bukhari that some scholars say that it is the *Deen*.

Abu Ayyub al-Ansari reported that the Messenger of Allah, may Allah bless him and grant him peace, said, "Four things are part of the *sunan* of the Muslims: circumcision, the tooth-stick, perfume and marriage." (Related by Ahmad and at-Tirmidhi)

'Uthaym ibn Kulayb reported that his grandfather went to the Prophet, who told him, "Shave off your unbeliever's hair and be circumcised". (Related by Ahmad, Abu Dawud and others, with a weak *isnad*)

Abu Barza said, "We asked the Messenger of Allah whether an uncircumcised man could perform *hajj* to the House of Allah, and he said, 'Not until he is circumcised.'"

'A'isha reported that the Messenger of Allah performed an *'aqiqa* for al-Hasan and al-Husayn and circumcised them on the seventh day. (Related by al-Hakim and al-Bayhaqi)

Regarding female circumcision, Abu'l-Malih ibn Usama reported from his father that the Prophet said, "Circumcision is a *sunna* for men and an honourable deed for women." (Related by Ahmad and al-Bayhaqi) This agrees with what I mentioned about the obligation of female circumcision in some rare cases in which the clitoris or labia are abnormal in size or thickness. That being the case, there is no doubt that it is more honourable and becoming for her from a sexual point of view, as is shown by the following *hadith* from as-Dahhak ibn Qays: "There was a woman circumciser in Madina called Umm 'Atiyya who used to circumcise girls. The Messenger of Allah said to her, "Umm 'Atiyya, cut slightly and do not overdo it because it brings radiance to the face and is more pleasant for the husband". Another narration has "Cut, but do not completely remove the part," meaning simply "cut off the extra unnatural piece." This *hadith* exists by another transmission, from Ibn 'Umar, as: "Women of the Ansar, use henna and circumcise, but do not overdo it: that is more pleasant for your husbands. Also beware of ingratitude for blessings." (al-Bazzar)

This is what the authentic sources say about circumcision in Islam. Besides showing the advisability and wisdom of male circumcision, it also agrees completely with medicine and science regarding female circumcision.

Imams and scholars differ on some aspects of circumcision. Ash-Shafi'i said that it is mandatory. Malik, Abu Hanifa and Imam Ahmad say that it is *sunna* for men and recommended for women. The Malikis also state that it is recommended to cut off a small piece of the woman's skin in front of the opening of the vagina. In their view, completely removing it prevents sexual pleasure and to let it remain gives more pleasure in intercourse, as is stated in the *hadith*. That is also the opinion of ash-Shafi'i, the Imam who considers circumcision mandatory for both males and females. According to him, it is mandatory for the man to cut off all the skin which covers the glans of the penis and for women to remove the protruding piece of skin to the front of the opening of the vagina, and he states that this is agreed upon.

This is what I can offer you concerning this important topic and I hope that I have amply studied it and explained it for you so that you will be able to arrive at your judgements free of prejudice and unaffected by the bias of tradition. I hope that it will move you to a sound and correct judgement, and that you will try to amend a widespread error in Egyptian society which has no basis in the *deen* or in science but is rather in conflict with them.

May Allah give us all success in ascertaining the truth purely for the sake of Allah.

PART III
The Islamic View on Female Circumcision

This section examines the opinions of several contemporary Islamic scholars concerning this matter, some of whom pronounce in favour of female circumcision and some of whom are more reserved in their opinion.

Shaykh Ibrahim Hamrush
Chairman of the Fatwa Committee of Al-Azhar

Continuing the custom unless it is proven harmful

The Arabs were practising circumcision when Islam came and the Muslims have continued the practice although there is some disagreement among *fuqaha'* concerning it. The Shafi'is believe that it is mandatory for both men and women. Their evidence is not uncontested. Ash-Shawkani said in *Nayl al-Awtar*, "The truth is that there is no sound proof that it is mandatory." The Malikis believe that circumcision is *sunna* for men and recommended for women. The Hanafis and Hanbalis believe that it is *sunna* for men and honourable for women.

The Hanafis and Hanbalis say that the reason for this difference is that in the case of the male the existence of the foreskin can harm the body and be a danger to health whereas this is not the case with the female, so her circumcision is not to avert harm or for health reasons. Nor is it true that failure to circumcise a female will stimulate her sexuality and corrupt her morals. If that were the case it would be either mandatory or a confirmed *sunna*.

So female circumcision does not remove harm or encourage health or preserve morals and honour. It is honourable for a woman to be circumcised, and so is good for this reason. To prohibit female circumcision I would need to be convinced by sound evidence that it causes harm to women. If it were prohibited, it would be prohibited but that is not the case, so the practice may be continued.

'Abdu'l-Wahhab Khallaf
Professor of Shari'a at the Law College of Cairo

A custom which can be abandoned if harmful

Muslim *fuqaha'* agree that it is *sunna* to circumcise boys. Female circumcision is said not to be *sunna* but a matter of honour, it is also held by some to be *sunna*. According to *Kitab ad-Durr al-Mukhtar* and the gloss of Ibn 'Abidin, pt. 5 p. 530: "The basis is that circumcision is *sunna* and one of the hallmarks of Islam and should only be abandoned if there is a valid reason, such as when circumcision will cause excessive pain to the child. Female circumcision is not *sunna* but a matter of honour." Ibn 'Abidin further says that the Prophet stated, "Male circumcision is *sunna* and the circumcision of women is an honourable act." "An honourable act" is explained as meaning one that gives increased pleasure to the man.

This makes it clear that doctors' opinions on female circumcision contradict no text in Islam and are not contrary to any judgement about which the Muslim *fuqaha'* agree. That obliges doctors to expand the scope of their research and not to condemn female circumcision on the basis only of isolated cases. They should compare circumcised and uncircumcised girls and then give their opinion. If they conclude that female circumcision is harmful and decide to forbid it on that basis, their prohibition will not contradict any religious text; nor will it go against the consensus of religious scholars.

'Allam Nassar
Mufti of Egypt

A pro-circumcision view

The Fatwa Committee responded to the question of female circumcision with a *fatwa*, recorded as no. 280/63, 11 December 1950, which states: "Female circumcision is one of the practices of Islam and forms part of the *Sunna* of the Prophet. The *fuqaha'* and Imams of the Muslims agree that it is allowed, but they disagree as to whether it is obligatory or *sunna*. For the *fatwa* we prefer to categorise it as *sunna* because the strongest and clearest transmission suggests that. The wisdom in it is that it brings about moderation of sexual desire in women and leads to a praiseworthy balance."

This is further explained in the magazine *Liwa' al-Islam*: "There many *hadiths* reported from the Messenger of Allah, may Allah bless him and grant him peace, which indicate that it is legal to circumcise females. There is the statement of the Prophet, 'Five are part of the *fitra*,' and he counted circumcision among them. This is a general statement applicable to both males and females. He also said, 'Whoever becomes Muslim should be circumcised.' Abu Hurayra also reported that the Prophet said, 'O women of the Ansar! Circumcise but do not overdo it.' There is also the *hadith*, 'Circumcision is a *sunna* in men and an honourable act in women.' From this it is clear that female circumcision is legitimate, and that it is one of the good things of the *fitra* and has a praiseworthy effect in making the woman balanced."

As for the medical opinions which were published in the magazine *ad-Duktur* and elsewhere regarding harmful effects of female circumcision, they are individual opinions which have no scientifically agreed foundation or established scientific basis. They admit that there has been no research on circumcised women, and that the occurrence of cancer in circumcised women is less than in uncircumcised women.

Some of those doctors explicitly aim at entrusting the procedure of female circumcision to doctors rather than ignorant women circumcisers so that the procedure may be safe and free from adverse health consequences. However, medical theories of illness and means of treatment are not established or firm. Indeed, they change with time and continuing research and it is not valid to rely on them in objecting to the circumcision which the Wise Lawgiver has deemed to contain a wisdom and improvement of human nature.

We know from experience that events over the passage of time show us the concealed wisdom of the Lawgiver in the rulings which he laid down for us and guided us in the *Sunna*. May Allah give us all success to the paths of guidance!

Muhammad al-Banna
Egyptian Deputy Minister for Religious Affairs

It should be linked to a benefit or abandoned

Legally, female circumcision is agreed upon by *Shari'a* scholars. The *fuqaha'* disagree about its exact status, some seeing it as obligatory and others as a *sunna*. I have researched what is reported about female circumcision in the *hadiths* of the Prophet and found that there were a number of *hadiths* related about it.

The first is the *hadith* of Umm 'Atiyya, a circumciser of women. It is related that the Prophet said, "Cut a little and do not overdo it." The second *hadith* is from 'Abdullah ibn 'Umar: "Circumcise, but do not overdo it and beware of ingratitude for blessings." The third is the *hadith* related by Ahmad and al-Bayhaqi, "Circumcision is *sunna* for men and honourable for women."

When I examined the *isnads* of these *hadiths* connecting them to the Messenger, may Allah bless him and grant him peace, it was clear that there is something wrong in all them: not one of them is completely sound. I do not want to go on at length here criticising these *isnads*. It is enough to say that this criticism has been carried out by some scholars who say that there is no report which can be relied on regarding circumcision and no *sunna* to be followed.

One thing which is clear from this is that is circumcision cannot be an undisputed part of the *deen* because there is certainly no consensus among scholars that it is desirable. My understanding is that it is not one of those matters which Allah has obliged us to follow whether there is apparent benefit or not, and since that is the case it must depend on whether there really are benefits in it. If there are recognisable benefits in it we should do it and if there are no benefits we should not.

In matters of this nature, it is necessary to refer to experts, including in this case doctors. But we must not refer to them alone as the magazine *ad-Duktur* has done. We should deal with the question through proper research by holding a conference where every doctor should give his opinion supported by evidence and then the others should argue with him until all reach a unanimous verdict informed by full investigation and a definitive position can be reached.

This question must be examined in an exhaustive way, dealing with all the factors involved. For instance, we should look at girls in cold climates and hot climates and ascertain the effect of that on the sexuality of the girl and her natural inclination for male company. That may well vary according to the country and climate concerned. It may also vary according to the development of the girls concerned. Some girls have an unusual physiognomy which must be rectified and some have a natural character which has no harm for them or harm for the men, in which case they should be left as Allah created them. A complete study of all this is needed so that the judgement is in accordance with the benefit.

The opinions of doctors who have dealt with this subject can be found in the pages of the magazine *ad-Duktur*. A number of them indicated what I have mentioned and recommended that girls be circumcised in some cases but recommended against it in others. These, however, only comprise a small group of doctors. When a large number participate in a conference along the lines I have indicated then the research will be more complete. In short, from a religious point of view the Muslims have choice. Circum-cision should not be performed if not doing so is the more beneficial course; but whether that is in fact the case needs first to be proper-ly ascertained by experts.

Muhammad Ibrahim Salim
Chairman of the Muslim Supreme Court

Another pro-circumcision view

1. Female circumcision was an ancient Arab custom which they inherited from their forefathers from the most ancient times. It was a sacred practice which they were eager to retain as they were keen on honour and nobility.

2. Islam came and confirmed this custom because of the benefit it contains both for the woman herself and society as a whole. It considered female circumcision to be a recommended and honourable practice. It is not obligatory, mandatory or *sunna* but it is recommended because of the good it does. There is no punishment for omitting it. Circumcision is *sunna* for men and honourable for women.

3. *Fuqaha'* agree that it is recommended to circumcise girls because it protects them from infection, swelling of external genitalia and excessive sexual desire which, if repressed, can lead to neurosis or, if unleashed, lead to the path of vice. This happens especially during youth when the hormones associated with reproduction are at their peak.

4. The circumcision which the Islamic *Shari'a* considers honourable is to cut the protruding part of the clitoris to lower its level so that it is not exposed to arousal while moving, rubbing against clothing, riding animals and other similar things. This is the reason for the word used for female circumcision, *khafd*, which means to lower the level.

51

5. There is no doubt that female circumcision done in this way – only removing the protruding part of the clitoris and letting the rest remain – brings good health and feminine grace to the girl and protects her morality, chastity and honour, maintaining within reason the necessary sexual sensitivity.

6. As for removing the entire clitoris and labia in the manner followed by ignorant villagers, the Islamic *Shari'a* does not condone it. It is considered a reprehensible innovation resulting in the total loss of female sexuality, which in turn leads to reluctance to participate in the means of procreation.

7. It is clear from the above that there are no grounds for the opposition of some doctors to the legitimate type of female circumcision. Perhaps their opposition lies in their false assumption that female circumcision is all done in the manner of ignorant peasants or by the barbaric method followed in some areas of Sudan.

Muhammad al-Laban

The custom has benefits unknown to reason

The monthly magazine *ad-Duktur* produced some studies which conclude that medical opinion does not support female circumcision, that it is not confirmed by the *Shari'a* in the Book or the *Sunna*. In spite of my respect for the researchers and my belief that scientific progress and research should illuminate culture and study, I will indicate to you the judgement of Islam as mentioned by the *hadiths* of the Prophet, the rulings of scholars and Imams, and the wisdom of the *Shari'a* laws on the subject.

The *hadiths* and traditions connected to it

Al-Bukhari transmitted in *al-Adab al-Mufrad* that Ibn Shihab said, "When a man becomes Muslim, he is commanded to be circumcised, even if he is old." This tradition confirms what ash-Shawkani mentioned. As-Subki transmitted from him from Abu Hurayra that the Prophet said, "If someone becomes Muslim he must be circumcised, even if he is old."

Imam Ahmad and al-Bayhaqi reported the *hadith* from Shaddad ibn Aws: "Circumcision is a *sunna* for men and an honourable act for women." The transmission is *marfu'*,[1] and there is further testimony from Ibn 'Abbas which supports it.

Al-Bukhari related in *al-Adab al-Mufrad* that Umm al-Muhajir said, "I was captured together with some girls from Byzantium. 'Uthman offered Islam to us, but only myself and one other girl became Muslim. He said, 'Circumcise them and purify them.' I used to work for 'Uthman."

1. 'elevated', a narration from the Prophet mentioned by a Companion, e.g. "The Messenger of Allah said…"

The legal status of male and female circumcision

Male circumcision is obligatory according to Imam ash-Shafi'i and other scholars including Imam Ahmad, and *sunna* according to Imam Malik and Abu Hanifa and the majority of scholars. Female circumcision is obligatory according to ash-Shafi'i and al-'Antara and *sunna* according to Imam Ahmad, Malik and Abu Hanifa. In short, circumcision of men and women is obligatory according to ash-Shafi'i and *sunna* according to Malik and Abu Hanifa, and, obligatory for men and *sunna* for women according to Ibn Hanbal and Yahya ibn Sa'id al-Ansari.

The time of circumcision

Some people say that the best time is the seventh day after birth, but Imam Malik and al-Hasan disapproved of circumcision on the seventh day because that is when the Jews perform it. The generally recommended time is before puberty. Al-Layth recommended between seven and ten years. Malik said that it is recommended when a child loses his milk teeth. It is considered mandatory when puberty comes. According to al-Juwayni, however, it should not be done before puberty because children are not obliged to perform bodily acts of worship, let alone to suffer pain.

Circumcision of adults who enter Islam

This is held either to be mandatory, because Ibrahim did it, or *sunna,* because 'Uthman commanded it as is related in the *hadith* of Umm al-Muhajir. Not doing it is based on what is related by al-Bukhari in *al-Adab al-Mufrad* from al-Hasan, "Are you not astonished at this man, meaning Malik ibn al-Mundhir? He went to some aged people of Kaskar who had became Muslim and examined them, and then gave orders that they be circumcised although it was winter. I heard that some of them died. Greeks and Abyssinians became Muslim with the Messenger of Allah, and they were not examined."

Conclusion

We can see from this that the legal ruling on circumcision has a higher status than recommendation but does not reach that of being mandatory, thus making it a confirmed *sunna*. This was the position which Imam ash-Shafiʻi adopted. It should only be left undone if there is a genuine reason for not performing it, such as illness. Medical opinions should not be used to abolish a pure *sunna* which has existed for 1400 years. The *hadith* of Umm ʻAtiyya al-Ansariyya makes that clear: "Cut a little and do not overdo it. It brightens the face and is more pleasant for the husband." There are various transmissions of this in which the wording varies slightly. The pleasure mentioned in the *hadith* about the husband and wife is the sexual pleasure which is the concern of the doctors. What is meant by 'cutting a little' and 'not overdoing it' is to cut off the protruding skin, avoiding complete excision.

Medicine has not discovered the source of the radiance which the Prophet mentioned, but *"he does not speak from whim."* (53:3) The explanation is that complete excision removes the sensations relayed from nerve-endings while cutting the skin has only a slight effect on the sensitivity. *Sunna* circumcision lets the blood vessels heal (which other types of circumcision do not) and makes purification easy once the extra skin is cut off because it is that which retains urine and menstrual fluid, preventing internal purity and leading to unpleasant smells.

It is enough for us that Allah made the Islamic *Shariʻa* the Final Law and valid until the end of time. Our human brains cannot possibly find fault with it or undermine its principles, which are the basis of all human rules. The Prophet, may Allah bless him and grant him peace, said, "The natural form of man (*fitra*) involves five things," and circumcision is one of them.

Mahmud Shaltut

No evidence for or against

Circumcision is an ancient practice which people trace back to the time of the Prophet Ibrahim. It was performed on both men and women. The Prophet, may Allah bless him and grant him peace, related a number of *hadiths* about it and *hadith* scholars agree on the soundness of some of them and the weakness of others. One of them on which is there is agreement is the saying of the Prophet, "The natural form of man (*fitra*) involves five things: shaving the pubic hair, circumcision, trimming the moustache, removing hair from the armpits and cutting the nails." He also said, "Ibrahim, peace be upon him, was circumcised."

Scholars say that the *fitra* is the ancient human pattern which the Prophets chose and on which religious laws agree. It is the natural imperative of the human form in respect of cleanliness and purity.

Traditions which the *hadith* scholars consider weak are these words attributed to the Prophet: "Whoever becomes Muslim should be circumcised"; his words to someone who was brought to him who had become Muslim, "Remove the hair of disbelief from yourself and be circumcised"; to the woman who circumcised other women, "Cut a little and do not overdo it"; and "Circumcision is a *sunna* for men and an honourable action for women."

Faced with these *hadiths*, the *fuqaha'* disagree about the legal status of circumcision since they do not have a clear definitive text related on the subject. Shafi'is believe that it is mandatory for men and women Hanbalis say that it is mandatory only for men. Hanafis and Malikis believe that it is *sunna* for men and honourable for women.

Imam ash-Shawkani said, after investigating the transmissions on the subject from the aspect of transmission and proof: "The truth is that there is no sound evidence that it is mandatory. It is certain that it is *sunna*, in view of the *hadith* 'The natural form of man involves five things,' and other such statements. So it is mandatory is to stop at what is certain until something is transmitted which obliges moving from it."

From this it is clear that there is no evidence to make circumcision more than *sunna*, and it is made general by the sound *hadith*: "The natural form of man involves five things," which means that as a *sunna* it applies equally to both males and females. Most schools, however, think that it is honourable for women and *sunna* for men. Perhaps this difference comes from something not mentioned in the *hadiths,* which is that the greater importance of circumcision for the male is made evident by the fact that the male foreskin readily secretes of impure discharges which could easily lead to infection and sepsis. There is another consideration indicated by Imam Ahmad who observed concerning the difference between male and female: "When a man is not circumcised skin hangs down over the end of the penis and is not pure."

The view of male circumcision among the Imams is that it is either mandatory or a confirmed *sunna*. It includes the consideration of preventing illness and impurity, with which the *Shari'a* is entirely concerned. *Fuqaha'* have said that it is one of the signs of Islam to the extent that if the people of a city or village decided to abandon it, the Imam should fight them. This applies only to men.

As for women, it has no hygienic consideration and so the ruling is below *sunna* and it is considered honourable. Perhaps that concerns the protruding piece of flesh which either the woman finds troublesome or the man is unused to and finds distasteful. Thus circumcision is honourable for women and at the same time honourable for men. Female circumcision in this respect is simply something which ensures psychological security and the continuance of affection between man and wife: it has the same status as her taking care of her beauty, dabbing perfume or removing underarm hair.

Some people consider female circumcision to be mandatory on the grounds that not being circumcised may increase a woman's sexual drive and induce her to act immodestly. If this view is to be accepted and ruling based on it, it must first be researched and studied. Lapses into immodest behaviour are also frequently found among circumcised women, as is known in crimes of honour, and the unknown lapes of this inevitably outnumber the known. The fact is that this does not result from lack of circumcision. It is a result, as Dr. Kawkab Hafni Nafis states, of sound health and the activity or weakness of glands, and then morals and environment, attention, care in education, supervision, close control, and not allowing the unrestrained mixing of the sexes which destroys chastity and honour.

Others believe that banning of circumcision would lead to men having to resort to drugs in order to satisfy the unweakened sexual drive of their wives and that circumcision is therefore obligatory in order to save men from taking these harmful drugs. The truth is that those who are accustomed to taking those drugs are only responding to their own personal sexual urges. Some of them take them because of an established habit and so it is like a necessary drug for them, as applies to tea-drinkers and smokers. So this does not provide an argument either for or against female circumcision. *Fuqaha'* who are not Shafi'is take the position that female circumcision is not mandatory or *sunna* but that it is honourable for men and women.

The *Shari'a* confirms the general principle that when it is established by means of meticulous investigation – not by opinions arising from personal whims or under pressure from the customs of certain people – that a particular thing is harmful to health or corrupts morals, then the *Shari'a* obliges that the action be prohibited to avert the harm or corruption it brings about. Until that is proven about female circumcision, it should be carried out according to popular custom under the auspices of the Islamic *Shari'a* as it has been with the knowledge of the men of the *Shari'a* from the time of the Prophet until today, on the basis that it is honourable to circumcise females, not mandatory or *sunna*.

As for the view of some non-Muslims that circumcision constitutes a "barbaric operation", it is my opinion that that expression is an exaggeration: the barbarity attributed to circumcision itself only applies when the procedure is carried out by ignorant women. This is due to negligence on the part of the authorities in supervising this matter and their failure to prevent those who do not perform the operation properly from performing it. The *Shari'a* confirms that this sort of thing must be stopped and circumcision taken out of the hands of quacks and ignorant surgeons. The authorities must safeguard the health of the people and protect them from being harmed by those who act badly in matters of public interest. Quacks must be punished if they contravene this.

This is what we believe to be the position in the *Shari'a* regarding circumcision according to the texts and comparison of the evidence.

Mahmud 'Arnus
Former Chairman of Legal Review

A sign of Islam

The word *khitan* (circumcision) refers both to the act of circumcision and to the place of circumcision, as in the *sahih hadith*, "When the two circumcised parts meet, ghusl is mandatory." In women it is called *khafd* (lowering).

The legal status of circumcision in Islam

Muslim scholars have discussed this matter at length. Their task is to clarify the legal rulings of Islam. There is no disagreement between them that circumcision is prescribed. They consider it part of the natural form on the grounds that Abu Hurayra related that the Messenger of Allah, may Allah bless him and grant him peace, said: "The natural form of man involves five things," and circumcision was one of them. Indeed, he made circumcision the first of the characteristics of the *fitra*. The *fitra* is the *Hanifiyya*, the religion of Ibrahim; and the chief element of the *fitra* in the body is circumcision.

According to *Tuhfat al-Wadud fi ahkam al-mawlud* by Ibn al-Qayyim, "The *fuqaha'* differ about the legal status of circumcision. Ash-Sha'bi, Rabi'a, al-Awza'i, Yahya al-Ansari, Malik, ash-Shafi'i, and Ahmad hold that it is mandatory, and Malik is so strict about this that he says, 'Anyone who is not circumcised is not permitted to be an imam and his testimony is not accepted.' Many *fuqaha'* transmit that Malik stated that it is *sunna*. According to Qadi 'Iyad, 'Circumcision is *sunna* according to Malik and most of the *fuqaha'*, but they consider it sinful to abandon the *sunna*, so it lies somewhere between obligation and recommendation.' Malik nonetheless clearly stated that the testimony of an uncircumcised man is not accepted nor is he permitted to be imam. Al-Hasan al-Basri and Abu Hanifa considered circumcision to be not mandatory, but *sunna*. Ibn Abi Musa, one of the disciples of Ahmad, also said that it is a confirmed *sunna*. Ahmad stated in a transmission, 'It is not mandatory for women.'"

Scholars relate a group of *hadiths* about circumcision from which some deduce that it is mandatory and others that it is *sunna*. Al-Khattabi said, "As for circumcision, even though it is mentioned as one of the *sunnas*, most scholars consider it mandatory because it is the distinguishing mark of the *deen* and by it the Muslim is known from the unbeliever. When a circumcised body is found in a group of slain people who are uncircumcised, the prayer is said for him and he is buried as a Muslim in a Muslim graveyard. So circumcision is the mark of the *Hanifiyya*, the religion of Ibrahim, and he made it practice to abide after him until Allah takes back the earth and those on it. Ibn al-Qayyim said, 'It is confirmed that all the Prophets descended from Ibrahim did it and recommended it, even the slave of Allah, His Messenger and Word, the son of Mary. He was circumcised to follow Ibrahim.'"

The time of circumcision

We read in *Nayl al-Awrar* by ash-Shawkani: "Circumcision is not limited to a particular time: this is the position of the majority. Hence it is not obligatory to carry out circumcision when someone is still a child, although Shafi'is consider it mandatory for a guardian to circumcise his ward before puberty. There is disagreement as to whether circumcision is obligatory. Imam Yahya related from al-'Antara and ash-Shafi'i and many scholars that it is mandatory for men and women. Like Malik, Abu Hanifa and al-Murtada, an-Nawawi said, "The statement of most scholars is that it is *sunna* for them." An-Nasir and Imam Yahya also declared it to be mandatory for men and women.

Imam Ahmad and al-Bayhaqi related the *hadith*, "Circumcision is *sunna* for men and honourable for women," and related from the Messenger of Allah that he said to Umm 'Atiyya, a female circumciser in Madina: "Cut a little and do not overdo it."

Al-Bazzar related as follows from the *hadith* of Nafi' from 'Abdullah ibn 'Umar from the Messenger of Allah: "O women of the Ansar! Use henna and circumcise, but do not overdo it. Beware of ingratitude for blessings." Ibn al-Qayyim said, mentioning Harb in his questions to Maymuma the wife of the Prophet, peace be upon him, that she told the female circumciser, "If you circumcise, then take a little and do not overdo it. It brightens the face and gives her more pleasure with the husband."

Abu Dawud related from Umm 'Atiyya that the Messenger of Allah said to the female circumciser, "If you circumcise, do not overdo it. That is more pleasurable for the woman with her husband." This signifies that when circumcision completely removes the clitoris the woman's desire will be weakened and her pleasure with her husband lessened, just as when it is left as it is and none of it is removed, it increases her lust. When some of it is taken and some left, that creates a balance.

The wisdom of circumcision

To explain the wisdom that underlies circumcision, scholars say that it is one of the distinguishing marks of the people of Islam, the dye of Allah and His *fitra* on which He formed people. It is the *fitra* of the *Hanifiyya*, the religion of Ibrahim. Circumcision also entails purification, cleanliness, beautification, improving nature, and reducing lust which, if not kept under control, reduces a person to the condition of an animal; but if the sexual appetite is not strong, circumcision reduces a person to a lifeless state. Circumcision achieves a balance. That is why we find that uncircumcised men have more lust than others, and the same applies to women. It also enhances radiance and luminosity of the face as mentioned in the *hadith* of Maymuna, the wife of the Messenger. Ibn al-Qayyim said, "The wisdom applies to male and female, although it is more evident where men are concerned." He added that this is *the dye of Allah – and who has a better dye than Allah?"* (2:138)

Allah has made circumcision a distinguishing mark for those who are devoted to Him and to His *deen* and described as His servants, so that when one does not know a person's religious state, it is possible to know it by the mark of circumcision. The Arabs used to be called "the nation of circumcision". People of different religions have distinguishing marks so that those people who do not have them are not considered one of them. Christians have baptism, and since the Christians want their children to be Christian they immerse them in water and claim that it purifies them. That is analogous to circumcision for the people of Islam. *"We have appointed for every nation a rite that they observe, so let them not dispute with you about the matter. Call the people to your Lord. You are guided straight."* (22:67)

Ibn al-Qayyim discussed this extensively in a chapter of his book *Tuhfat al-mawdud fi ahkam al-mawlud* (which is translated at the end of this book).

Dr. Zakariyya al-Birri
Head of the Department of Shari‘a in the Law College of Cairo

Female circumcision: what is the legal status of female circumcision and is it necessary?

The best-known opinion of Muslim scholars is that female circumcision is not a religious duty as some *fuqaha'* say and that it is only honourable, meaning an action which it is good to do in moderation without excessive or complete excision. The following statement of the Messenger, may Allah bless him and grant him peace, to that effect is related: "Circumcision is a *sunna* for men and honourable for women," as is his command to Umm ‘Atiyya to perform female circumcision without going to excess or excising completely.

It is clear that balance and not going to excess is more pleasant for the woman and for the one who marries her, meaning better for both of them, since it should result in their chastity and fulfilling their desires without excess or deficiency. Some scholars believe that many women have no need of circumcision because of a natural balance in their physique and the lack of the extra protruding part which is circumcised.

In addition to this it is known that some women in various places go to excess in female circumcision. In such cases it becomes illegal. Furthermore, despite the claims made by some people, chastity and honour, and strength or weakness of desire are not in fact contingent on circumcision or lack of it. In the light of this fact it is clear that those who do not do it commit no sin.

64

'Abdu'r-Rahman al-'Adawi

Professor at the College of Islamic Da'wa, al-Azhar

It prevents a woman falling into what is forbidden

In relation to female circumcision, the *fuqaha'* agree that it is honourable for a woman. What is meant by its being honourable is that it helps her preserve her honour and restrains the drives which produce excessive sexual desire. In eastern lands, where the climate is hot for most of the year, a girl may easily become aroused if she is not circumcised and this may make her shameless and prey to her sexual desires, except those to whom God shows compassion. So circumcision is honourable for a woman in order to help her to maintain her morals and chastity and to safeguard her against having an over-developed sexual drive.

Circumcision in the Shari'a of Islam is honourable and no harmful consequences whatsoever result from it when it is done according to the way that the Messenger of Allah indicated when he said to the female circumciser: "Circumcise, but do not overdo it." This is the middle way in which there is neither excess nor deficiency.

This method strikes the right balance in female circumcision and forestalls the attack of those doctors who say that circumcision leads to stress on the man in conjugal relations with his wife, causing him to take drugs to delay orgasm so that the couple coincide and there is complete harmony between them. This position is taken by doctors in the face of the unacceptable form of female circumcision, since what they warn against only happens when the operation of circumcision takes the form of complete excision in which the entire clitoris is removed. That, however, is not the procedure which the Messenger of Allah prescribed. The harmful effects mentioned are the result of incorrect practices in circumci-

65

sion and have no bearing on the legal status of circumcision as such.

That is why I think that the health authorities and the Colleges of Medicine should become involved in preventing errors in the procedure of female circumcision by training nurses who will perform circumcision properly. That involves the teaching and training of nurses in nursing schools and centres of higher education so that we may have a number of nurses who can carry out circumcision in the proper manner according to the *deen* and correct medical practice in the way which produces benefit for both the man and the woman concerned.

Postscript

A number of opinions about female circumcision have been presented since the publication of these articles, and since the author's intention is to present a wide-ranging selection of positions on the issue of female circumcision it behoves us to mention them here.

One argument proposes that Allah does not like mutilation. This is put forward by Doctor Nawal El-Saadawi who states that Allah could not have created an organ simply for the sake of its complete removal. Others have pointed out that what may be involved is a justification of ancestral practices by attributing benefits to them, real or fictitious, whereas proponents have pointed out that the attack on circumcision is a case of one set of cultural values attacking another, with which it disagrees, without proper investigation and analysis.

It has also been pointed out that we have no direct record of either the daughters or granddaughter of the Prophet or indeed of any of the wives or female relations of the Prophet or his Companions, being circumcised. Indeed, the words of the Prophet may be understood as moderating a pre-Islamic custom which was still being practised rather than advocating it.

Yet it is clear from what has been said above that circumcision of males is something that should be done unless there is real danger to the health of the person concerned; and in the case of females it is permitted, provided it is done in the strictly limited way indicated by the Prophet, may Allah bless him and grant him peace. Any extreme form of female circumcision such as complete excision of the clitoris or infibulation is forbidden.

Part IV
The Circumcision of Children and its Legal Rulings

by Ibn al-Qayyim al-Jawziyya

We conclude this book clarifying the rulings of the *deen* regarding the circumcision of boys and girls with an abridgement of Chapter Nine of *Tuhfat al-mawdud fi ahkam al-mawlud* (The Gift to the Beloved on the Rulings concerning Children) by Ibn al-Qayyim al-Jawziyya, which deals with the circumcision of boys and girls and expounds the rulings of circumcision under the following headings.

Section 1: An explanation of the meaning and derivation of the words used for circumcision

Section 2: The circumcision of the Prophet Ibrahim and the Prophets after him

Section 3: The legality of circumcision and its being one of the characteristics of the *fitra*

Section 4: The disagreement as to whether it is obligatory or recommended

Section 5: On the time when it becomes mandatory

Section 6: The disagreement concerning disapproval of circumcision on the seventh day

Section 7: The wisdom and benefits of circumcision

Section 8: Details of the amount to be removed in circumcision

Section 9: The ruling about circumcision includes both males and females

Section 10: The ruling concerning the liability of the circumciser in the event of complications arising from circumcision

Section 11: Rulings on the prayer, purity, sacrifices and testimony of uncircumcised people

Section 12: Circumstances which remove the obligation

Section 13: The Prophet's circumcision

Section 14: On the Divine wisdom in the sons of Adam being resurrected uncircumcised

The author of this book, Muhammad ibn Abi Bakr az-Zura'i, known as Ibn al-Qayyim al-Jawziyya, was a famous scholar and *mujtahid*.

✳✳✳✳✳

In the course of the discussion, certain categories of *hadith* are mentioned in respect of evidence. They are:

- **marfu':** 'elevated', a narration from the Prophet mentioned by a Companion, e.g. "The Messenger of Allah said..."

- **mawquf:** 'stopped,' narration from a Companion which is his own statement. It can be elevated to *marfu'* if it is of the nature of "We were commanded to..." and similar expressions.

- **mursal:** a *hadith* in which a man in the generation after the Companions quotes directly from the Prophet without mentioning the Companion from whom he received it.

Section 1: An explanation of the meaning and derivation of the words used for circumcision

Khitan is the word used for the action of the circumciser. It is a verbal noun and is also used to designate part that is circumcised, as in the *hadith*: "When the two circumcised parts meet, then *ghusl* becomes mandatory." (Related by al-Bayhaqi) It is called *khafd* (lowering) in respect of women. *Khatana* is what is done to a man and *khafada* to a woman.

In the *Sahih* collections, Abu 'Ubayda said: "I circumcised the girl and boy," using the word *i'dhar*, but it is usually it is *khafada* for a woman. The foreskin (*qulfa* or *ghuzla*) is the skin which is removed. The Arabs claim that when a boy is born in the last phase of the moon his foreskin dissolves and so he becomes like someone who has been circumcised. Male circumcision entails cutting around the glans of the penis which is that part of the penis on which all the rulings are based once it has disappeared inside the vagina. There are more than three hundred rulings based on that – some say almost four hundred.

As for female circumcision, it entails the excision of a piece of skin somewhat like a tiny coxcomb to the front of the opening of the vagina. When the glans disappears inside the vagina, it is said that the circumcised part of the man meets together with the circumcised part of the woman.

Section 2: The circumcision of the Prophet Ibrahim and the Prophets after him

In the two *Sahih* collections it is reported from Abu Hurayra that the Messenger of Allah, may Allah bless him and grant him peace, said, "Ibrahim was circumcised at the age of eighty with an adze (*qadum*)." (al-Bayhaqi). According to al-Bukhari the word *qadum* refers to the name of the place where it happened.

Al-Marwazi said, "Abu 'Abdullah was asked whether Ibrahim circumcised himself with an adze. He said, "With the side of an adze." Abu Dawud, 'Abdullah ibn Hanbal and Harb said that they asked Ahmad about this and he replied that Qadum is a place.

Some reported it as Qadum, which is definitely a placename, and others reported it as *qaddum* which is the name of a tool. The story of the circumcision of Ibrahim is reported in a way which might appear to be contradictory but there is no contradiction involved, praise be to Allah. We will mention the various accounts.

In the *Sahih* of al-Bukhari there is a *hadith* of Abu'z-Zinad from al-A'raj from Abu Hurayra that the Prophet said, "Ibrahim circumcised himself at the age of eighty with an adze," and in a variant, "Ibrahim circumcised himself after eighty at Qadum." We find something similar in the *hadith* of Yahya ibn Sa'id from Ibn 'Ajlan from his father from Abu Hurayra and Yahya who said that the word means an adze. An-Nadr ibn Shumayl said: "He cut it with an adze." He was told that Qadum is a town in Syria but he did not accept that inference and stood by what he had said. The sound position is that the word used in the *hadith* means a type of tool: this is based on the following report from al-Bayhaqi.

Abu 'Abdullah and Abu Sa'id ibn Abi 'Umar reported from Abu'l-'Abbas Muhammad ibn Ya'qub from Muhammad ibn 'Abdullah from Abu 'Abdu'r-Rahman al-Muqri from Musa ibn 'Ali who said: "I heard my father say, 'Ibrahim the Friend was commanded to circumcise himself when he was eighty years old.

He made haste and circumcised himself with an adze and the pain he felt was intense. His Lord called him and revealed to him, 'You hastened to do it before We commanded which tool was to be used.' He said, 'My Lord, I disliked to delay fulfilling Your command.'" He said, "Isma'il was circumcised when he was thirteen years old and Is'haq when he was seven days old.'"

Ibn Hanbal reported with an *isnad* from Abu Hurayra that the Prophet said, "Ibrahim was the first to be circumcised when he was about 120. He was circumcised with an adze then lived for eighty years after that." But this *hadith* is defective. Yahya ibn Sa'id reported it from Sa'id ibn al-Musayyab from Abu Hurayra. This is also from the transmission of Abu Uways 'Abdullah ibn 'Abdullah al-Madani. Muslim related it in his *Sahih* as evidence and the people of the four *Sunan* report it. According to Abu Dawud it is sound. The transmission of it varies from Ibn Ma'n. Ad-Duri reported it as a weak *hadith* but according to a different report he considered it reliable. Al-Mughira ibn 'Abdu'r-Rahman, Shu'ayb ibn Abi Hamza and others related it from Abu'z-Zinad in a different form from Abu Uways. The transmitters of the *Sahih* reported that Ibrahim was circumcised when he was eighty. This is more likely to be correct and carries more weight than the *marfu'* and *mawquf* transmissions.

Some authorities reply that both transmissions are sound and the two can be reconciled as regards the lifespan of Ibrahim: he lived for 200 years, eighty of them uncircumcised and 120 circumcised. He was ordered to be circumcised when he was eighty. The second *hadith* reports that he was circumcised when 120 years remained of his life. There is a point which reconciles the two: he said, "The first man to be circumcised was Ibrahim when he had 120 years remaining," and he did not say "**at** 120".

The point is that circumcision is one of the things by which Allah put Ibrahim to the test. He carried out all of them perfectly and so Allah made him an Imam for all mankind. It is related that he was the first person to be circumcised and, as we have seen, it is found in the *Sahih* that Ibrahim was circumcised when he was 80 years old. Circumcision continued to be practised after his time among the Messengers and their followers. The Messiah was circumcised. Christians admit this, and they also admit that he forbade pork, forbade working on the Sabbath, prayed towards the Rock, and did not fast forty days, which is what they call the Great Fast or Lent.

In the *Jami'* of at-Tirmidhi and the *Musnad* of Ahmad we find a *hadith* from Abu Ayyub who reported that the Messenger of Allah, may Allah bless him and grant him peace, said, "Four things are part of the *sunan* of the Messengers: modesty, perfume, the tooth-stick and marriage." Az-Zuhri said, "This is a *gharib hasan hadith*." They disagree about its exact form. Some say the first thing was "*haya*" (modesty) and some say "henna"; but I heard our shaykh Abu'l-Hajjaj al-Mizzi say that both are wrong and that it should be circumcision. He said: "That is how al-Muhamili related it from the shaykh who related it from at-Tirmidhi himself. He said, 'It is circumcision: this is more likely than modesty or henna. Modesty is a quality and henna is not one of the *sunan*. The Prophet did not mention it among the qualities of the *fitra* or recommend it as he did circumcision.'"

On self-circumcision

According to al-Marwazi, Abu 'Abdullah was asked about someone circumcising himself and he said, "If he is strong." Al-Khallal reported that Abu 'Abdullah was asked about a man circumcising himself and he said, "If he is strong enough to do it." It is reported that Abu 'Abdullah was asked about a woman who is not circumcised when her husband comes to her: must she be circumcised? He replied, "Circumcision is a good *sunna*." He was asked a similar question to that of al-Marwazi about self-circumcision by a woman if she is strong enough to do it. He replied, "I do not like it." He was asked about a man circumcising himself and said, "If he is strong enough to do it, it is good and it is a good *sunna*."

Section 3: The legality of circumcision and its being one of the characteristics of the *fitra*

In the two *Sahih* collections we find the *hadith* of Abu Hurayra who reported that the Messenger of Allah said, may Allah bless him and grant him peace, "The natural form of man (*fitra*) involves five things: circumcision, shaving the pubic hair, trimming the moustache, cutting the nails, and removing hair from the armpits." (al-Bukhari) He made circumcision the first of the characteristics of *fitra*, and they are part of the *fitra* because the *fitra* is the *Hanifiyya*, the religion of Ibrahim. Ibrahim was commanded to adopt these characteristics and they constitute the words with which his Lord tested him, as mentioned by Ibn 'Abbas in commentating on this *ayat* (2:124): "He was tested by ten acts of purification: five relating to the head and five to the body. Those of the head are trimming the moustache, rinsing the mouth, snuffing water up the nose, using the tooth-stick and parting the hair; and those of the body are cutting the nails, shaving the pubic hair, circumcision, removing hair from the armpits, and washing away traces of faeces and urine with water."

There are two kinds of *fitra*: one connected with the heart, which is recognition and love of Allah and preferring Him over all else, and another with action, which are the characteristics under discussion. The first is to purify the *ruh* and to cleanse the heart. The second is to purify the body. Each of them helps the other and strengthens it. The highest aspect of the *fitra* of the body is circumcision, as will be mentioned in Section 7.

According to the *Musnad* of Imam Ahmad, 'Ammar ibn Yasir reported that the Messenger of Allah, may Allah bless him and grant him peace, said, "Part of the *fitra* is rinsing the mouth, sniffing up water, trimming the moustache, using a tooth-stick, cutting the nails, washing the knuckles, removing hair from the armpits, shaving pubic hair and circumcision." Cleanliness and purification are part of the *fitra,* as is the removal of those filthy excretions with which Shaytan is comfortable when they remain near the human being. He has a direct connection with the uncircumcised as we will see in Section 7.

Another of the early Muslims said, "Whoever prays, performs *hajj* and is circumcised is a *hanif*." So *hajj* and circumcision are the signs of the *Hanifiyya*. It is "the *fitra* on which Allah formed mankind."

Section 4: The disagreement as to whether it is obligatory or recommended

The *fuqaha'* differ about the legal status of circumcision. Ash-Sha'bi, Rabi'a, al-Awza'i, Yahya al-Ansari, Malik, ash-Shafi'i, and Ahmad consider that it is mandatory, and Malik is so strict about this that he says, "Anyone who is uncircumcised is not permitted to act as imam and his testimony is not accepted." Many *fuqaha'* transmit that Malik regarded it as *sunna*. According to Qadi 'Iyad, "Circumcision is *sunna* according to Malik and most of the *fuqaha'*, but they consider it sinful to abandon the *sunna*. So it is somewhere between obligation and recommendation. Malik nonetheless clearly stated that the testimony of an uncircumcised man is not accepted nor is he permitted to act as Imam." Al-Hasan al-Basri and Abu Hanifa declared it to be not mandatory but *sunna*. Ibn Abi Musa, one of the adherents of Ahmad ibn Hanbal, also called it a confirmed *sunna*. Ahmad stated in another transmission, "It is not mandatory for women."

Those who consider circumcision mandatory have many reasons for doing so. The first is the words of the Almighty, *"Then We revealed to you: 'Follow the religion of Ibrahim, a man of pure natural belief. He was no idolater.'"* (16:123) Circumcision is part of the religion of Ibrahim.

The second reason is what Imam Ahmad related from Abu Kulayb who went to the Prophet, may Allah bless him and grant him peace, and declared, "I have become Muslim." He said, "Remove the hair of disbelief from yourself." In other words, he said: "Shave." Another man who was with him said that the Prophet told someone else, "Remove the hair of disbelief and get circumcised." (Related by Abu Dawud, from Muhammad ibn Mukhallad from 'Abdu'r-Razzaq) He took it as being recommended to remove hair and that what the other man said is not binding.

The third reason is that Harb said in his Questions from az-Zuhri that the Messenger of Allah, may Allah bless him and grant him peace, said, "Whoever becomes Muslim should be circumcised, even if he is old." Even though this is a *mursal* hadith, it can be relied on.

The fourth reason lies in the fact that al-Bayhaqi reported that 'Ali said, "In the scabbard of the sword of the Messenger of Allah we found written on a page: 'An uncircumcised man is not left alone in Islam until he is circumcised even if he is eighty.'" Al-Bayhaqi said that only the People of the House have this *isnad*.

The fifth reason is based on what Ibn al-Mundhir related from Abu Barza from the Prophet about the uncircumcised: "He should not perform *hajj* to the House until he is circumcised." It says: "We asked the Messenger of Allah whether an uncircumcised man can make *hajj* to the House of Allah." He replied, "Not until he is circumcised." Ibn al-Mundhr then said, "It is not confirmed because it has an unknown *isnad*."

The sixth reason is from Ibn 'Abbas: "The prayer of the uncircumcised person is not accepted, nor are his sacrifices to be eaten." Imam Ahmad reported from Ibn 'Abbas, "Do not eat the sacrifice of anyone who is uncircumcised." Hanbal said in his *Questions* from 'Ikrima, "Do not eat the sacrifice of anyone who is uncircumcised." Al-Hasan did not accept what 'Ikrima said. He said, "'Ikrima was asked if he could make *hajj*. 'No,' he replied." According to Hanbal, "Abu 'Abdullah said, 'His sacrifices should not be eaten and his prayer and *hajj* are invalid until he is purified. It is part of the perfection of Islam." Again according to Hanbal, Abu 'Abdullah stated, "Someone who is uncircumcised cannot sacrifice, nor should his sacrifice be eaten, nor is his prayer accepted." 'Abdullah ibn Ahmad reported that Ibn 'Abbas said, "The prayer of the uncircumcised is not valid, his sacrifices should not be eaten, and his testimony is not allowed." Qatada observed that "Al-Hasan did not accept that."

The seventh reason is that circumcision is one of the marks which distinguish the Muslims from the Christians and so its obligation is of the same nature as that of the *witr*, *zakat* on horses, of *wudu'* for someone who laughs in the prayer, or is cupped, vomits or has a nose-bleed, the obligation to perform *tayammum* up to the elbows and strike the earth twice, and other such things. The obligatory status of circumcision is more apparent and stronger and so the Muslims barely consider someone who is not circumcised to be one of them. This is why one group of *fuqaha'* believe that the adult should be circumcised, even if that should result in his death, as is mentioned in Section 12.

The eighth reason is that anyone who does not accept it truncates the *Shari'a* of Allah and does not believe in its totality; hence it is obligatory, like cutting off the hand of the thief.

The ninth reason is that one is permitted to uncover his private parts for the purpose of circumcison without there being the need to urinate or for medical treatment or sexual relations with his wife. If it were not obligatory, this would not be permitted, because no *haram* act is made obligatory in order to maintain a *sunna*.

The tenth reason is that it involves abandoning two obligations and committing two forbidden acts. The one being circumcised has to uncover his private parts while the circumciser, who is unrelated to him, has to look at them. If it were not obligatory this would never be permitted.

The eleventh reason is the argument al-Khattabi uses for a proof. He said, "As for circumcision, even though it is mentioned as one of the *sunan*, most scholars consider it mandatory because it is the distinguishing mark of the *deen* and by it a Muslim is known from an unbeliever. When someone circumcised is found in a group of slain people who are uncircumcised, the prayer is said for him and he is buried among the Muslims."

The twelfth reason is that a guardian is legally allowed to cause pain to his ward by it, even at the risk of his death, and to pay from his property the cost of circumcision. If it were not mandatory, he would not be permitted to do any of these things.

The thirteenth reason that if it were not obligatory, it would not be permitted for the circumciser to carry it out, even if the one to be circumcised or his guardian permitted it. For no one is permitted to cut off a part of the body which Allah and His Messenger have not commanded to be cut off. No one is permitted, for instance, to cut off an ear or a finger. Having permission to do it does not remove from the one who does the sin of doing so; there is disagreement as to whether they are liable to make reparation.

The fourteenth reason is that uncircumcised men are liable to have their purity and prayer vitiated. If the foreskin covers the penis urine may get under it and prevent it being properly purified; which means that the soundness of purification and prayer are in fact based on circumcision. This is why many of the first and later Muslims forbid uncircumcised men to act as imam, placing them in the position of someone suffering from incontinence and the like. One of the purposes of circumcision is to avert the danger of urine being retained in the foreskin, so vitiating purity and the prayer. This is why Ibn 'Abbas said that Imam Ahmad and others related, "His prayer is not accepted." This is why the obligation to circumcise is annulled by death, since the obligations of purification and the prayer no longer apply.

The fifteenth reason is that lack of circumcision is a sign of the cross-worshippers and fire-worshippers who thereby distinguish themselves from the *hanifs*. Circumcision is a basic mark of the *hanifs*. This is why the first man to be circumcised was the Imam of the *hanifs*, Ibrahim, and circumcision has become a mark of the *hanifs*. It is part of what the children of Isma'il and the children of Israel inherited from Ibrahim the Friend. So it is not permitted to follow the cross-worshippers. Circumcision is a sign of their disbelief and trinitarianism.

The contrary evidence of those who hold that circumcision is not obligatory

Those who hold that it is not obligatory say that the *Sunna* itself states that it is only a *sunna*, as is made clear in the *hadith* of Shaddad ibn Aws from the Prophet who said, "Circumcision is *sunna* for men and an honourable act for women." Imam Ahmad related this *hadith*. They contend that the Messenger connected it to *sunnas* rather than to obligations. These are to shave the pubic hair, trim the moustache, clip the nails and pluck the armpits. They say that al-Hasan al-Basri remarked, "People became Muslim with the Messenger of Allah, may Allah bless him and grant him peace

– black and white, Greek, Persian and Abyssinian – and none of them was examined."

Imam Ahmad reported from al-Hasan, "Is not this man, meaning the amir of Basra, astonishing? He met some of the old men of Kaskar and asked, 'What is your religion?' 'Muslims,' they replied and he ordered that they be examined and found that they were uncircumcised. They were circumcised in the winter; I heard that some of them died. Greeks and Abyssinians became Muslim with the Messenger of Allah, and none of them were examined."

The people who take this position say that those who cite as evidence the following words of Allah: *"Then We revealed to you: 'Follow the religion of Ibrahim, a man of pure natural belief; he was not an idolater.'"* (16:123) and *"...For I have left the religion of a people who are clearly not believers in Allah and disbelieve in the Afterlife. I hold fast to the creed of my forebears Ibrahim and Ishaq and Ya'qub. We attribute no partners to Allah...."* (12:37-38) are wrong to do so. They claim that the word "religion" in these *ayats* refers to the fundamentals of faith, repentance to Allah, and sincerity of the *deen* for Allah. The Messenger of Allah, may Allah bless him and grant him peace, taught his Companions to say, "We follow the *fitra* of Islam, the word of sincerity, the *deen* of our Prophet Muhammad and the religion of our father, Ibrahim, a *hanif* and Muslim who was not an idolater."

The same scholars argue that if actions are included in the word "religion" they must refer to what Ibrahim did, and so we should act in the way in which he acted. If he did it as an obligation then we should follow him in that; but if he did it as a recommended action then following him means giving it the same status. So the question is whether the action was obligatory or recommended for Ibrahim. There is a well-known dispute about this but the most widely held position is that it is recommended since it cannot clearly be shown to be an obligation. So if we want to follow Ibrahim we must consider circumcision to be a recommended act and not an obligatory one.

They say that in the *hadith* of 'Uthaym ibn Kathir ibn Kulayb related from his grandfather, "Remove the hair of disbelief and get circumcised," Ibn Jurayh said that he reported it from 'Uthaym ibn

Kathir. According to Abu Ahmad ibn 'Adi, "This is what Ibn Jurayh said concerning this *isnad*: 'I reported from 'Uthaym ibn Kathir who was related to by Ibrahim ibn Abi Yahya.' He used the *kunya* of the name with Ibrahim. Specialists in *hadith* agree that it is weak, with the sole exception of ash-Shafi'i."

As regards the *mursal hadith* of az-Zuhri from the Prophet, may Allah bless him and grant him peace, "Whoever becomes Muslim should be circumcised, even if old," they consider the *mursal hadiths* of az-Zuhri to be the among the weakest and as unsuitable to be used as evidence, quoting several authorities in support of their position. As for the evidence to support adopting the dictum of Ibn 'Abbas that 'The sacrifice of the uncircumcised should not be eaten nor is his prayer accepted,' they observe that it is the solitary statement of a single Companion.

The statement that circumcision is one of distinguishing marks of Islam is true and there is no argument about it. But not all such marks constitute obligatory actions. Some are obligatory, such as the five prayers, *hajj*, fasting and *wudu'*; others are merely recommended, such as the *talbiya*, driving the sacrificial animals and garlanding them; and the status of the remainder, such as the *adhan*, the *'Ids*, sacrifices and circumcision, is a matter of dispute.

As for the argument that the permissibility of uncovering the private parts without the need for urination or medical treatment or sexual relations constitutes evidence for the obligatory nature of circumcision, the fact that the private parts are uncovered does not make this the case. It is permitted by consensus to uncover them for reasons other than obligatory ones. Also, the face of the woman is a private part, and yet she is permitted to uncover it in transactions which are not obligatory and for testimony against her when it is not obligatory.

The statement that "by it the Muslim is known from the unbeliever. When someone circumcised is found in a group of slain people who are uncircumcised, the prayer is said for him and not them" is not entirely true. Some unbelievers – the Jews, for instance – are circumcised and so circumcision does not distinguish between Muslims and unbelievers except in places where only the Muslims are circumcised. But that does not necessarily make circumcision mandatory, since many other things which distinguish a Muslim from a non-Muslim are not mandatory.

The fact that a guardian is permitted in the case of circumcision to cause pain to his ward and expose him to death and pay for it out of his property does not indicate that it is obligatory, since he is also permitted to cause him pain by disciplining him to correct him and to pay from his property the wage of a teacher and the price of a sacrifice he carries out on his behalf. Al-Khallal said, "Harb ibn Isma'il reported to me: 'I asked Ahmad, "Is one permitted to sacrifice on behalf of an orphan?" He replied, "Yes, when he has property." That is what Sufyan ath-Thawri said. Ja'far ibn Muhammad an-Nisayburi said, "I heard that Abu 'Abdullah asked about the bequest of an orphan and whether sacrificial animals can be purchased on his behalf. He remarked, 'Yes, they may be purchased for him.'""

The argument that it would not be permissible to cut off part of the body if it were not an obligation is refuted by the fact that lancing cysts, amputating dead limbs, pulling teeth, piercing the skin for cupping, cauterisation, and other medical procedures are certainly permitted. Such procedures are permitted on the basis of the clear benefit in them, not on the basis of being obligatory.

The impurity argument does not hold water either. It would be blameworthy if it were avoidable; but people are not blamed for things which it is beyond their power to avoid, and such things as incontinence of urine, incontinence of prostatic fluid and nosebleeds do not vitiate their purity. In such cases people cleanse themselves with stones or water to the best of their ability and are not taken to task for anything over which they have no control.

The argument that the fact that the cross-worshippers and fire-worshippers are uncircumcised makes it obligatory for Muslims to be differentiated from them by circumcision is refuted by the fact that this is by no means their only distinguishing feature. They are distinguished by all their false beliefs. The fact that a Muslim may reemble them in not being circumcised does not mean he agrees with them in other deviant aspects of their religion.

Refutation of the evidence of those who say that it is not mandatory

Those who affirm that circumcision is obligatory say that it is the sign of the *hanifs*, the distinguishing mark of Islam and the peak of the *fitra*. The Prophet, may Allah bless him and grant him peace, said, "Whoever does not trim some of his moustache is not one of us," and so what can be said of someone who neglects circumcision and is content to be uncircumcised like the cross-worshippers? One thing which clearly distinguishes worshippers of the All-Merciful from cross-worshippers is circumcision, and the *hanifs* have continued to practise it from the time of Ibrahim until the time of the Seal of the Prophets, who was sent to complete the *Hanifiyya* faith and affirm it without changing or altering it.

Allah commanded His Friend to be circumcised, knowing that His command would be obeyed, and one is not permitted to neglect it or ignore it. Ibrahim hastened to do what he was commanded to do by Allah and he circumcised himself with an adze in his eagerness to obey His Lord, making it an abiding *fitra* after him until the earth and everyone on it is inherited by Allah. All the Prophets from his descendants passed on the practice to their communities, including the son of the Virgin Mary who was circumcised following the tradition of Ibrahim. The Christians admit that and acknowledge that it is one of the commandments in the Gospel. But they followed the whims of people who were misguided before that and misled many and were misled from the Straight Path.

Then the scholar of the Family of the Messenger of Allah, 'Abdullah ibn 'Abbas, made an announcement that was heard by the elite and the common people: "The prayer of the uncircumcised man is not accepted, nor are his sacrifices to be eaten." He transmitted it from a group of the people of Islam. Such a thing would never be said of someone who disregarded something about which he had a choice. It could only be said about something known to be obligatory.

The fact that it is the foremost of the characteristics of the *fitra* on which Allah fashioned His servants, and to which all the

Messengers are called, is more than enough to make it obligatory. Anyone who does not do it is outside the *fitra* which Allah sent His Messengers to perfect. Whoever dies having failed to do it by delaying when he should have made haste to do it has renounced the religion of his father Ibrahim. *"Who would deliberately renounce the religion of Ibrahim except someone who reveals himself to be a fool? We chose him in this world and in the Next World he will be one of the righteous. When his Lord said to him, 'Submit!' He said, 'I have submitted myself to the Lord of all the worlds.'"* (2:130-131)

Al-Bayhaqi reported from Ibn 'Abbas, "The sacrifice of an uncircumcised person is not to be eaten nor is his prayer accepted nor is his testimony allowed." Then he said, "This indicates that he considered it mandatory." His words, "Circumcision is *sunna*" indicates that it is the *sunna* of the Messenger of Allah, may Allah bless him and grant him peace, and that the Messenger of Allah made it a *sunna* and commanded it. Hence it is mandatory. "The *Sunna*" means "the Way." One says, "I made such a *sunna* for you," meaning "I prescribed it." The words, "Circumcision is *sunna* for men" means that it is prescribed for them, not that it is merely recommended.

The *sunna* is the path followed in obligation and recommendation, for the Prophet said, "Anyone who renounces my *sunna* is not of me" (al-Bukhari and Muslim); and also "You must adhere to my *Sunna* and the *Sunna* of the Rightly-guided Caliphs after me." (Related by Ibn Hanbal, at-Tirmidhi, Abu Dawud and Ibn Majah) Ibn 'Abbas said, "Whoever opposes the *Sunna* is an unbeliever". The *sunna,* in the specific terminology of *hadith*, means something that may be left undone. Otherwise, the *sunna* is what the Messenger of Allah made *sunna* for his community. So the *Sunna* is the Way, which is the *Shari'a*, the Road and the Way.

So the fact that the Messenger of Allah, may Allah bless him and grant him peace, linked circumcision with *sunan* does not necessarily contradict its being mandatory. Some of the actions mentioned in *hadiths* are certainly mandatory, such as rinsing the hands and sniffing up water in *wudu'*, and cleansing with water in the lavatory, whereas some are recommended, like using the tooth-stick. Clipping the nails becomes obligatory when the nails are very long and clipping the moustache also becomes mandatory when it is too long, as the Messenger of Allah indicated when he said: "Whoever does not trim some of his moustache is not one of us."

The answer to the statement of al-Hasan al-Basri that "People became Muslim with the Messenger of Allah and none of them were examined" is that they did not need to be examined because they practised circumcision. All the Arabs used to practise circumcision and the Jews were all circumcised. It was known by any Christians who entered Islam and others that a sign of Islam was circumcision. They hastened to be circumcised after they became Muslim, just as they did to perform *ghusl*. Some of them were old and it would have been hard on them and fatality would have been a distinct possibility had their foreskins been removed. Imam Ahmad said, "As for an adult who becomes Muslim, if it is feared that circumcision may kill him, he has a dispensation."

The word "religion" cannot be restricted to faith alone. It refers to the *deen* as a whole and is therefore the sum of actions and faith. The religion of Ibrahim is the natural form of man which is the *deen*. It is impossible that Allah would command that the religion of Ibrahim be followed in word alone. He circumcised himself in obedience to the command of his Lord who tested him by it. If we do not do it as he did it, we cannot be said to follow him.

The *hadith* related by 'Uthaym ibn Kulayb can be relied on if there is some other evidence to strengthen it, and these *marfu'*, *mawquf*, and *mursal hadiths* strengthen one another. The same applies to the case with the discussion on the *hadith* of Musa ibn Isma'il and others like it. The fact that the statement about the sacrifices of an uncircumcised man not being eaten and his prayer not being accepted comes from Ibn 'Abbas alone, making it the statement of a single Companion, does not invalidate its use as evidence. The four Imams and others used the statements of the Companions as evidence and they explicitly stated that they are evidence. Ash-Shafi'i went further and considered opposition to them to be innovation.

It is true that distinguishing marks are divided into what is recommended and what is mandatory; but abandoning that which distinguishes the worshippers of the Merciful from cross-worshippers and perfects purification is not something to be done lightly. The truth is that circumcision is one of the most important mandatory acts.

As regards uncovering the private parts for circumcision, if the benefit did not outweigh than the potential harm of uncovering them, looking at them and touching them, it would not be permitted. If circumcision were only recommended, that would entail uncovering the private parts for something for which there is no necessity, and that would not be permissible.

The contention that the fact that a guardian can also use an orphan's property to pay the wage of a teacher shows circumcision not to be obligatory is not applicable, because there is no doubt that teaching is an obligatory duty for all guardians. He may only spend his ward's money on things which are necessary for his benefit in this world and the Next. If circumcision were purely recommended, expenditure on it would have the status of voluntary *sadaqa* and should not be met from the orphan's property. The same applies to sacrifices. They should only be paid for out of an orphan's wealth if it is obligatory for him to make them.

Section 5: On the time it becomes mandatory

The time at which circumcision becomes mandatory is puberty, it is at puberty that acts of worship become obligatory; while before that they are not obligatory. In the *Sahih* of al-Bukhari according to a *hadith* narrated by Sa'id ibn Jubayr Ibn 'Abbas was asked how old he was when the Messenger of Allah died, may Allah bless him and grant him peace. He said, "We were circumcised at that time, and they did not circumcise a man until he reached puberty." There is some disagreement about the age of Ibn 'Abbas when the Prophet died. According to az-Zubayr and al-Waqidi he was born in the ravine before the Banu Hashim left it three years before the *Hijra,* in which case he would have been thirteen when the Messenger of Allah died.

Sa'id ibn Jubayr reported from Ibn 'Abbas: "The Messenger of Allah, may Allah bless him and grant him peace, died when I was ten, and I had read the *Mufassal.*" Abu 'Umar said, "We reported that from him through various lines of transmission." 'Abdullah ibn Ahmad reported from his father from Sulayman ibn Da'ud from Shu'ba from Abu Ishaq, 'I heard Sa'id ibn Jubayr relate that Ibn 'Abbas said, "The Messenger of Allah died when I was fifteen.' 'Abdullah stated that his father said, 'That is correct.'"

We find in the two *Sahih* collections from Ibn 'Abbas, "I came riding on a mule – and at that time I was close to puberty – while the Messenger of Allah, may Allah bless him and grant him peace, was leading the people in prayer at Mina with nothing in front of them, and I passed between some of the rows." Most biographers say that he was thirteen when the Prophet died. He was born in the ravine. That was three years before the *hijra*. The Messenger of Allah was in Madina for ten years. It is said that he was circumcised then.

The statement of Ibn 'Abbas that "they did not circumcise a man until he reached puberty," resembles the words of the Almighty: *"But when they have reached the end of their waiting-*

89

period either retain them with correctness and courtesy or part from them with correctness and courtesy" (65:2) inasmuch as it indicates the outer limits. So the implication of the statement of Ibn 'Abbas is that children were circumcised before puberty. Ibn 'Abbas meant that he had already been circumcised before the day the Prophet died. He reported that during the *Hajj* of Farewell, which was eighty days before the Prophet died, he was close to puberty.

Section 6: The disagreement about disliking the seventh day

Disagreement with the view disapproving of it is based on two positions which are both related from Imam Ahmad. He said in the chapter on the circumcision of the child: "Abdu'l-Malik ibn 'Abdu'l-Hamid reported, 'I asked Abu 'Abdullah when a child should be circumcised. He replied, "I do not know, and I have not heard anything on the subject." I said, "It is hard and severe for a child of ten." I told him that my son Muhammad was five and I wanted to circumcise him. I noticed that he seemed to approve of that and that he seemed to dislike doing it at ten because it would be harsh and severe for the child. He told me, "I think that that is hard on the child, and I do not think that it is wrong for a child of a month old or a year old." He said no more about that except that I saw that he was surprised that anyone should cause pain to a child.'"

'Abdu'l-Malik said, "Al-Hasan disliked a child being circumcised on the seventh day." Muhammad ibn 'Ali as-Simasar said that Muhanna said, "I asked Abu 'Abdullah about a man who circumcised his son on the seventh day. He disliked it and said, 'That is what the Jews do.' Ahmad ibn Hanbal told me that al-Hasan disliked a man to circumcise his child on the seventh day. I asked, 'Who transmitted it from al-Hasan?' He replied, 'Some of the Basrans.' Ahmad said to me, 'I heard that Sufyan ath-Thawri asked Sufyan ibn 'Uyayna, "At what age should a child be circumcised?" He replied, "At the same age at which Ibn 'Umar circumcised his sons."' Ahmad said to me 'Sufyan ibn 'Uyayna was never cleverer than when he said, "At the same age at which Ibn 'Umar circumcised his sons."'"

'Isma ibn 'Isam reported from Hanbal that Abu 'Abdullah said, "There is nothing wrong with a child being circumcised on the seventh day. Al-Hasan disliked it in order that there should be no resemblance to the Jews but there is nothing binding in this."

Muhammad ibn 'Ali reported from Salih that he told his father, "A child should be circumcised on the seventh day." He related from al-Hasan that he said that that was what the Jews did. He said, "Wahb ibn Munabbih was asked about that and said, 'It is recommended on the seventh day because it is easier for the child. When children are born their bodies lack sensation and they do not feel any pain on the seventh day. If they are not circumcised then, we leave them until they become strong.'"

Ibn al-Mundhir said that there is disagreement about the best time for circumcision, and that some people disapproved of children being circumcised on the seventh day. Al-Hasan al-Basri disapproved, as did Malik ibn Anas, in order to be different from the Jews. Ath-Thawri said, "It is dangerous."

According to Malik, the correct position is to act differently from the Jews. He said, "What usually happens in our land is that circumcision is carried out when a child loses his milk-teeth."

Ahmad ibn Hanbal said, "I have not heard anything about that." Al-Layth ibn Sa'd said, "Circumcision for a boy should take place between seven and ten years." He said that he related from Makhul from someone else that Ibrahim the Friend of the Merciful circumcised his son Ishaq at seven days and circumcised his son Isma'il when he was thirteen years old. Abu Ja'far said, "Fatima used to circumcise her children on the seventh day."

According to Ibn al-Mundhir, "There is no firm prohibition concerning this matter and there is no tradition to refer to about the best time for circumcision or the age at which it has been performed. Things are basically permitted and it is not permitted to forbid anything except with evidence. There is no evidence forbidding that children be circumcised on the seventh day."

In the *Sunan* of al-Bayhaqi there is a *hadith* narrated by Zuhayr ibn Muhammad from Muhammad ibn al-Munkadir from Jabir from the Messenger of Allah about al-Hasan and al-Husayn being circumcised on the seventh day. There is also a *hadith* of Musa ibn 'Ali ibn Rabah from his father stating that Ibrahim circumcised Ishaq when he was seven days old and that Isma'il was circumcised at puberty. So the age at which Ishaq was circumcised became a precedent among his descendants and that of Isma'il among his. But Allah knows best.

Section 7: The wisdom and benefits of circumcision

Circumcision is one of the embellishments of the laws which Allah Almighty has prescribed for His slaves, by which He completes the outward and inward beauty of mankind. It completes the *fitra* on which He formed man. That is why it is part of the full primordial faith, the religion of Ibrahim. The basis of the legality of circumcision is its connection with Ibrahim. When Allah made a covenant with Ibrahim and promised to make him an imam for mankind and that he would be the father of many peoples and that the Prophets and kings would come from his loins, He informed him that He was placing among his descendants a distinguishing sign: that they should circumcise every child among them so that the covenant would be marked on their bodies. Circumcision is a sign of entering into the religion of Ibrahim, and this tallies with the interpretation that it is circumcision which is referred to in the words of the Almighty: *"The dye of Allah – and what dye could be better than Allah's?"* (2:138)

Circumcision has the same status that baptism has for the cross-worshippers. Their claim is that they purify their children by immersing them in the water of baptism and they say, "Now he is a Christian." Allah Almighty prescribed for the *hanifs* the dye of the *Hanifiyya*, and made its sign circumcision: *"The dye of Allah – and what dye could be better than Allah's?"* Allah Almighty assigned signs to those linked to Him by which they are known. This is why people brand their cattle and other livestock by a brand so that they will be marked as belonging to their owners. That this brand is then inherited by one community after another.

Allah made circumcision a sign of those who adhere to Him and His *deen*, those who are described as His worshippers, so that when one is ignorant of the state of a person, it can be known by the sign of circumcision. The Arabs used to be called the "nation of circumcision". This is why the *hadith* of Heraclius states, "I dreamt that the kingdom of circumcision was victorious," and the companions of Heraclius told him, "Do not let this worry you. The Jews are circumcised, so kill them."

While they were doing that, the emissary of the Messenger of Allah arrived with his letter and Heraclius ordered that he be examined to see whether he was circumcised and they found that he was. When he told Heraclius that the Arabs were circumcised, the emperor observed, "It must be the king of this nation." When the Battle of Ajnadayn took place between the Muslims and Byzantines. Hisham ibn al-'As began to shout, "O company of Muslims! The uncircumcised have no steadfastness against the sword!" He was reminding them of the sign of the *deen* of the cross-worshippers.

What is meant is that the "dye of Allah" is the primordial faith by which people's hearts are dyed with His gnosis and love, sincerity towards Him, and worship of Him alone with no partner. The "bodily dye" consists of the characteristics of the *fitra*: circumcision, shaving the pubic hair, clipping the moustache, cutting the nails, removing hair from the armpits, rinsing the mouth, sniffing up water, using the tooth-stick and cleansing the excretory orifices with water. So the *fitra* of Allah appears both in the hearts and on the bodies of *hanifs*.

According to Muhammad ibn Jarir at-Tabari, the words of Allah "the dye of Allah" refer to Islam. That is because when the Christians want to make their children Christians, they place them in their fonts and claim that that is something that will purify them, analogously to the position of circumcision in Islam. It is the "dye" which marks their entrance into Christianity. Allah Almighty told His Prophet, may Allah bless him and grant him peace: When the Jews and Christians say, *"'Be Jews or Christians and you will be guided.' Say, 'Rather adopt the religion of Ibrahim, a man of natural pure belief. He was no idolater.'"* ... and so on, up to His words, *"The dye of Allah – and what dye could be better than Allah's?"* (2:138)

Qatada said, "The Jews dye their sons as Jews and the Christians dye their sons as Christians, but the dye of Allah is Islam, and there is no dye better or purer than Islam." Mujahid said: "The dye of Allah is the *fitra* of Allah." Another said, "It is the *Deen* of Allah."

Circumcision also entails purification, cleanliness, adornment, improving nature, and reducing lust which, if not kept under control, reduces people to the condition of animals. If, however, the sexual appetite is insufficient, circumcision can reduce people to a lifeless state.

This is why someone may be cursed and verbally abused for being the son of an uncircumcised woman, alluding to her lust. What beautification is better than reducing what is too long and excessive in the form of the foreskin, pubic hair, the hair of the armpits, the hair of the moustache, and long nails? Shaytan conceals himself under all these things, is at home with them, and lives in them. He blows into the outer opening of the urethra of uncircumcised men and the vagina of uncircumcised women, which he is unable to do when they are circumcised. He conceals himself in the pubic hair and under the nails.

The foreskin is uglier than long nails, a long moustache and long unkempt pubic hair. Anyone with sound awareness will see that the foreskin is ugly and that removing it is a factor in improvement, cleanliness and beautification. This is why Allah tested his Friend Ibrahim by ordering him to remove these things – which he did – and so He made him an Imam for mankind.

Another aspect of circumcision is the radiance of the face which is visible when it is done and the dullness that you see when it is not done. Harb mentioned in his Questions that Maymuna, the wife of the Prophet, told the female circumciser, "If you circumcise, then take a little and do not overdo it. It is gives radiance to the face and gives her more pleasure with her husband."

Abu Dawud related from Umm 'Atiyya that the Messenger of Allah, may Allah bless him and grant him peace, commanded the female circumciser: "If you circumcise, do not overdo it. That is more pleasurable for the woman and preferable for the husband." The meaning of this is that if the circumcision procedure completely removes the clitoris, the woman's desire will be weakened and her pleasure with her husband lessened, just as if it is left as it is and none of it removed, it increases her libido. When some of it is taken and some left, that brings about a balance in physiology and libido.

Furthermore it is undeniable that cutting the flesh is a sign of slavehood. You will find that cutting the tip of the ear, branding the forehead and similar things are done to many slaves as a sign of their slavehood so that if they run away they can be returned to their master on the evidence of that mark. So it cannot be denied that cutting this fleshy extremity is sign of slavehood in relation to Allah so that may people know that the one who has had it done is one of the worshippers of Allah, the *hanifs*. Circumcision is therefore a sign of this *sunna* and there is nothing nobler than that, to say nothing of the purification, cleanliness, adornment and balanced libido that it entails.

It is said with regard to the wisdom of female circumcision, that when Sara gave Hajar to Ibrahim and she became pregnant, Sara became jealous and made an oath to cut three parts of her flesh. Ibrahim was afraid that Sara would mutilate her nose and cut off her ears, so he commanded her to pierce her ears and circumcise her, and that became a *sunna* among women afterwards. This is not denied by anyone; it is also accepted that the origin of *sa'y* was Hajar's running between the two hills seeking food for her son, and that the *jamarat* originated with the pebbles that Isma'il threw at Shaytan when he went with his father. Allah prescribed for His slaves that they remember and revive the *sunna* of Ibrahim and establish his memory and esteem his slavehood towards Allah. And Allah knows best.

Section 8: Details of the amount to be removed in circumcision

According to Abu'l-Barakat in *Kitab al-Ghaya,* in male circumcision the whole of the foreskin should be removed. If only the greater part is taken, that is allowed. In female circumcision it is recommended not to overdo it. It is related from 'Umar that he said about female circumcision: "If you circumcise, let some of it remain."

Al-Khallal said in his Collection concerning what should be cut off in circumcision, "Muhammad ibn al-Husayn informed me that al-Fadl ibn Ziyad said, 'Ahmad was asked, "How much is cut off in circumcision?" He replied, "Enough to allow the glans to show.""'"

'Abdu'l-Malik al-Maymuni reported: "I said, 'Abu 'Abdullah, there is a question I have been asked about circumcision: what happens when a child is circumcised and it is not done thoroughly?' He said, 'The circumcision is enough if half or more of the glans of the penis shows.' Then he observed to me, 'If it is less than half, I am afraid.'"

Ibn ad-Dabbagh says in *ash-Shamil*: "The obligation for the man is to cut off the skin over the glans of the penis so that the whole glans is exposed. As for the woman, she has two parts which are to be cut: one is her hymen and the other is that part that needs cutting, which resembles a coxcomb, to the front of the opening of the vagina between the labia. When it is cut, its root remains like a date pit."

Al-Juwayni says in his *Nihaya*: "It is recommended for men to cut off the foreskin, which is the skin which covers the glans of the penis. The whole glans of the penis should be visible. It must be cut so that no skin remains hanging loose."

Ibn Kajj said, "I think it is enough to cut off part of the foreskin, even if only a little, provided that the cutting goes all around the tip."

According to al-Juwayni: "The amount recommended in female circumcision is that to which the word *khafd* is applied: in other words, to reduce the height. In the *hadith* it is the amount indicated in the command to make it slight according to the words of the Prophet, "Take a little and do not overdo it," meaning "leave the fleshy part protruding."

Al-Mawardi said, "The *sunna* is to remove the skin completely from the glans of the penis, and the minimum condition is that nothing should be left covering the very end of the penis. In the case of women, it is to cut off the skin in the vagina to the front of the opening of the vagina and urethra, at the base of which is something which is like a date stone, and to remove the skin above that."

Section 9: The ruling about circumcison includes both males and females

Salih ibn Ahmad, in discussing when a man has intercourse with his wife and does not ejaculate, said, "When the two circumcised parts meet, then *ghusl* is mandatory." Ahmad said, "This shows that the women used to be circumcised." He was asked about a man who goes to his wife and finds that she is not circumcised: is it mandatory for her to be circumcised? He said, "Circumcision is *sunna*."

Al-Khallal said that Abu 'Abdullah was asked whether a woman whose husband comes to her and finds that she is not circumcised must be circumcised. He was silent and turned to Abu Hafs. "Do you know anything concerning this?" he asked. "No," he replied. He was told that the husband had been with her for thirty or forty years without saying anything about it. He was asked, "If she is strong enough to be circumcised?" He said, "Good."

It is reported that Muhammad Yahya al-Kahhal said, "I asked Abu 'Abdullah about a woman being circumcised. He said, 'I have transmitted knowledge about it.' Then he said, 'I looked and found the report of the Prophet, "When the two circumcised parts meet," and two circumcised parts are mentioned, not one.' I told Abu 'Abdullah, 'So it must be.' He said, 'It is more compelling as regards the man. That is because if the man is not circumcised that skin might hang over the end of the penis and he cannot avoid what is there. That does not apply so much in the case of women.' I said, 'There is no dispute that it is recommended for women, but there is disagreement as to whether it is obligatory.'"

There are two transmissions on the subject from Ahmad. One states that it is mandatory for men and women and the second only that it is only obligatory for men. The evidence for this is the *hadith* of Shaddad ibn Aws: "Circumcision is *sunna* for men and honourable for women." There is a difference between men and women. This statement is used as evidence that the command to do it has come for men as Allah Almighty commanded His friend who performed it in obedience to His command.

As for female circumcision, its original cause was the oath of Sara, as has already been stated. Imam Ahmad said, "The female circumciser should not cause harm," going by what Ibn 'Umar told the circumciser, 'Let some of it remain if you circumcise.'" Imam Ahmad mentioned from Umm 'Atiyya that the Messenger of Allah instructed the female circumciser, "If you circumcise, do not over-do it. That is more pleasurable for the woman and better for the husband." The wisdom which we have mentioned as existing in circumcision includes males and females, but is clearer in the case of the male. But Allah knows best.

Section 10: The ruling concerning the liability of the circumciser in the event of complications arising from circumcision

Allah Almighty said, *"There is no way open against the good-doers."* (9:91) In the *Sunan,* from a *hadith* narrated by 'Amr ibn Shu'ayb from his grandfather, we learn that the Prophet, may Allah bless him and grant him peace, said "Anyone giving medical treatment but not recognised as a practitioner of medicine is liable." In the event of the circumciser becoming liable, he or his relatives (*'aqila*) are liable for it, as for any other injury. If the compensation amounts to more than a third of the blood-money, the debt is owed by the relatives. If it is less than a third, it is taken from his own property. If someone dies of complications and the circumciser is not a professional in this craft and is not known for skill in it, then he is liable because it is a complication arising from a wound caused by an operation which he had no authority to carry out. People agree that there is liability for inflicting an injury, and they disagree on other matters.

According to Ahmad and Malik, there is no liability for any harmful consequences resulting from administering a *hadd* or punishment, since no one is liable for the harmful consequences of something he has been given permission to do, such as any harmful consequences from consummating a marriage or complications arising from venesection, cupping, circumcision, lancing a boil, or cutting a cyst, which are permitted for someone who is skilled in such surgical procedures.

According to ash-Shafi'i, someone officially assigned to do it is not liable for the consequences of a *hadd* punishment or retaliation, but someone who has not been assigned is liable because death caused thereby is evidence of transgression and injustice. According to Abu Hanifa, complications arising from an obligation do not incur liability, whereas complications resulting from retaliation do incur liability because it is permitted to proceed only when someone's health permits.

The sound *sunna* is contrary to this position. If the circumciser knows the craft, circumcises the child at a normal age, and does it properly, all agree that he is not liable for any complications resulting from the wound such as occur when a circumcised person is made ill by the procedure and dies. If someone gives a circumciser permission to circumcise them when it is very hot or very cold or they are in a state of weakness in which their health is endangered and they are sane and adult, he is not liable because having been granted permission to do it absolves him from responsibility. If the person is under age, he is liable since the permission of such a person has no legal standing. There some controversy as to the position when his guardian gives permission. Who is liable, the guardian or the circumciser? There is no doubt that the guardian is the instigator and the circumciser is the direct cause. The legal principle demands that the direct cause be held liable because he could have delegated the action to someone else. In a different situation, however, it is impossible to hold him liable if there was no possibility of his being able to assign it to someone else. Such are the various rulings about complications arising from circumcision. And Allah knows best.

Section 11: The rulings about the prayer, purity, sacrifices and testimony of uncircumcised people

Al-Khallal reported that Ibn 'Abbas said, "The prayer is not accepted from uncircumcised people and their sacrifices are not to be eaten." According to Waki', when an uncircumcised man comes of age and is not circumcised, his testimony is not accepted. Jabir ibn Zayd also reported that Ibn 'Abbas said, "The sacrifices of an uncircumcised man are not to be eaten."

Hanbal said in another place, reporting from 'Ikrima, "The sacrifices of uncircumcised people may not be eaten." He said that al-Hasan disagreed with what 'Ikrima said. 'Ikrima was asked, "Can he perform *hajj*?" He replied, "No."

Hanbal reported that Abu 'Abdullah said, "His sacrifices are not to be eaten and his prayer and *hajj* are not accepted until he is pure. It is part of the perfection of Islam." Elsewhere, Hanbal stated that Abu 'Abdullah said, "An uncircumcised man does not sacrifice, nor are his sacrifices eaten; and his prayer is invalid."

It is reported from Jabir ibn Zayd that Ibn 'Abbas said, "The prayer is not valid for the uncircumcised man and his sacrifices are not to be eaten nor is his testimony permitted." According to Qatada, al-Hasan did not accept that.

Ishaq ibn Mansur said, "I asked Abu 'Abdullah, 'And the sacrifices of the uncircumcised?' He said, 'There is nothing wrong with them.'"

Abu Talib said, "I asked Abu 'Abdullah about the sacrifices of uncircumcised people and he said that Ibn 'Abbas was very strict about their sacrifices."

Al-Fadl ibn Ziyad said, "I asked Abu 'Abdullah about the sacrifices of uncircumcised people and he answered that it is related from Ibrahim, al-Hasan and others that they did not consider there to be any harm in them, apart from what is related from Jabir ibn Ziyad from Ibn 'Abbas about disapproving of it."

Abu 'Abdullah said, "This is hard for people: if a man becomes Muslim when he is old and they fear that circumcision may endanger him, are his sacrifices still not to be eaten?"

Al-Khallal mentioned that Ahmad ibn Hanbal was asked about the sacrifices of uncircumcised people and the *hadith* of Ibn 'Abbas was mentioned to him. Ahmad said, "As I see it, if a man is born of two Muslim parents, how can he not be circumcised? As for an adult, when he becomes Muslim and fears that circumcision may endanger his life, I think he has a dispensation." Then he mentioned the story of al-Hasan about the amir of Basra who circumcised men in winter, some of whom died. Ahmad said, "If an adult becomes Muslim and he fears for himself, I think he has an excuse for not being circumcised."

Section 12: Circumstances which remove the obligation

There are various things which remove the obligation to undergo circumcision.

Being born without a foreskin

If a man is born without a foreskin he does not need to be circumcised since he does not have that which makes it necessary. This is agreed upon. But some later people say that it is recommended to run the razor over the place because that is all one can do to carry out the command. Said the Prophet, may Allah bless him and grant him peace, "When you are commanded to do something, carry out as much of it as you can."

The correct position is that this is disapproved of and does not bring one near to Allah. It is not an act of worship and has nothing to do with the *Shari'a,* since it is worthless and without benefit. Using a razor is not the goal but a means to achieve the goal. If the goal is annulled, there is no sense in using the means. Some people say, in rather the same way, if someone has no hair on his head, it is recommended for him to run a razor over his head after the *hajj*!

Among the Arabs, when a boy was born without a foreskin they claimed that if he was born during the last phase of the moon his foreskin would decrease shrivel up, saying "the moon has circumcised him." To be born without a foreskin is in fact very rare, and in any case the foreskin is never completely absent: the end of the glans protrudes, revealing the place where the urine emerges and so making circumcision still necessary in order to make the full glans show. Only if the entire glans is visible does one not have to be circumcised at all. Muhammad ibn 'Uthman al-Khalili the *muhaddith* informed me in Jerusalem that it he was born like that. And Allah knows best.

Weakness

A second reason for being excused from circumcision is if a child is too weak to bear it so that it is feared that it will cause his death and he continues to be fragile. This is an valid excuse. It is still obligatory, but the obligation is cancelled by inability on his part, just as applies to other obligations.

Age and fear

A third excuse applies if a man becomes Muslim when he is old and fears the consequences of circumcision for his health. This removes the obligation from him according to the majority of scholars. Imam Ahmad said something to that effect, which was transmitted by a group of his companions, and mentioned the statement of al-Hasan that Greeks, Abyssinians and Persians became Muslim in the time of the Messenger of Allah, may Allah bless him and grant him peace, and none of them were examined. Sahnun ibn Sa'id, the famous Maliki scholar who compiled the *Mudawwana*, disagreed with the majority and did not waive circumcision for an adult who fears for himself. That is also one position in the school of Ahmad as related by Ibn Tamim and others.

What our fellow-scholars say means that the obligation to undergo circumcision is only removed by fear of death – which means that it should not be done then and in such a case it is not permitted. This is stated clearly in the commentary on *al-Hidaya*. There are many similar cases, including washing with cold water when it is very cold or someone is ill, a sick person fasting when it is feared that he may die because of fasting, carrying out the *hadd* on a sick person or a pregnant woman. All of these excuses actually make the action forbidden as well as annulling the obligation.

Death

The fourth reason not to circumcise is death. That it is not mandatory to circumcise a dead person is agreed by the whole

Community. The majority of scholars hold that it is not even recommended, and that is the position of the four Imams. Some later Imams mentioned it as being recommended and made an analogy based on trimming the moustache, shaving the pubic hair, and removing the hair of the armpits: things that are done in the case of the dead. This is contrary to the practice of the Community, and the analogy is false. Trimming the moustache, clipping the nails and shaving pubic hair are all part of full purity and removing dirt and impurity.

Circumcision entails cutting off a piece of flesh and the reason for which it is prescribed applies only during one's lifetime. Once someone has died there is no benefit in circumcision. The Prophet, may Allah bless him and grant him peace, reported that he will be resurrected on the Day of Rising uncircumcised. What, then, is the use of cutting the foreskin from someone when he is dead when he will be resurrected on the Day of Rising with it in place?"

Postscript

Ihram does not render circumcision unlawful. There is a clear text on it from Imam Ahmad. When asked whether a *muhrim* may be circumcised, he said, "Yes." He did not put circumcision in the same category as removing hair and clipping nails, whether in life or after death.

Section 13: The Prophet's circumcision

There is disagreement about the circumcision of the Prophet. One view is that he was born circumcised; the second is that Jibril circumcised him when he opened his chest; and the third is that his grandfather 'Abdu'l-Muttalib circumcised him according to the normal practice of the Arabs with their sons. We will mention the people who made these statements and their evidence.

Those who say that he was born circumcised rely on the use of *hadiths* as evidence. One of them is related by Abu 'Umar ibn 'Abdu'l-Barr, according to whom it is said that the Prophet, may Allah bless him and grant him peace, was born circumcised. This is found in the *hadith* which 'Abdullah ibn 'Abbas related from his father al-'Abbas ibn 'Abdul-Muttalib who said, "The Messenger of Allah, may Allah bless him and grant him peace, was born circumcised and with his umbilical cord cut. His grandfather 'Abdu'l-Muttalib was amazed and said, 'Something important will come from this grandson of mine.'"

Ibn 'Abdu'l-Barr also said, "The *isnad* of this *hadith* from al-'Abbas is not sound. It is related as *mawquf*, stopping at Ibn 'Umar, and does not establish anything." I said: "We related the *hadith* of Ibn 'Umar by way of Abu Nu'aym with an *isnad* which goes back to Ibn 'Umar who said, 'The Prophet, may Allah bless him and grant him peace, was born circumcised.' However, one of the links in this *isnad*, Ibn Sulayman al-Baghandi, is weak. According to ad-Daraqutni, he often concealed faults in the *isnad*, relating what he did not hear; he may have stolen this *hadith*.'"

Another source is related by al-Khatib with his *isnad* from the *hadith* of Sufyan ibn Muhammad al-Massisi with an *isnad* stemming from Anas ibn Malik, who said: "The Messenger of Allah, may Allah bless him and grant him peace, stated, 'One aspect of the honour bestowed on me is that I was born circumcised and no one saw me.'" Al-Khatib added, "No one related the *hadith* in this form except Yunus from Hushaym. Only Sufyan ibn Muhammad al-Massisi has it. It is a *munkar* (denounced) *hadith*." According to al-Khatib, ad-Daraqutni was asked about Sufyan ibn Muhammad al-Massisi, and he replied that he was a shaykh of the people of Massisa called Sufyan ibn Muhammad al-Fazari. He was a weak transmitter with a bad state. Salih ibn Muhammad said, "Sufyan ibn Muhammad al-Massisi is of no consequence."

Abu'l-Qasim ibn 'Asakir reported by way of al-Hasan ibn 'Arafa that Anas said that the Messenger of Allah said, may Allah bless him and grant him peace: "Part of the honour my Lord Almighty granted me is that I was born circumcised and no one saw my private parts." There are a number of unknowns in the *isnad*. Abu'l-Qasim ibn 'Asakir said, "Ibn al-Jarud stole and was a liar. Transmitters relate from him from al-Hasan ibn 'Arafa."

Also adduced as evidence for this position is a statement which Muhammad ibn 'Ali al-Hakim at-Tirmidhi mentioned in his *Miracles of the Prophet*. He said, "One of them is that Safiyya bint 'Abdu'l-Muttalib said, 'I wanted to know if whether he was a boy or a girl, and I saw that he was circumcised.' This *hadith* is not established and it has no known *isnad*. Abu'l-Qasim 'Umar ibn Abi'l-Hasan stated in a book he wrote about the circumcision of the Messenger that it is traced to Muhammad ibn Talha in the form cited by him. In this book he stated that the Messenger of Allah, may Allah bless him and grant him peace, was born circumcised. This Muhammad ibn 'Ali al-Hakim at-Tirmidhi was not one of the specialists in *hadith*, and he had no knowledge of its methods or skill."

In his book he discussed the indications of Sufism and the *tariqas*, unveiling deep matters and realities so that the discussion went beyond the rules of the *fuqaha'* for which he should be attacked and rebuked. The Imams of both the *fuqaha'* and the Sufis attacked him on that account and said that he had ceased to conduct himself in a pleasing manner. They said that he had introduced into the science of the *Shari'a* something which would divide the community and that made it necessary to attack and express disapproval of him. He filled his book with forged *hadiths* and packed it with reports which are not transmitted or heard.

He alleges, for instance, in a book of his called *al-Ihtiyat*, that the Prophet prostrated the two prostrations of forgetfulness after every prayer he prayed, even if he did not forget any of it. That is not permitted by consensus. Anyone who does it is charged with excess and innovation. Something else that he related was that Safiyya said, "I saw him circumcised", which contradicts the other *hadiths* where he says "No one saw my private parts." So each *hadith* about this subject contradicts another and none of them are established. Even if he was born circumcised, this is not one of his special qualities. Many people are born without needing to be circumcised.

Abu'l-Ghana'im, the Zaydi genealogist, mentioned that his father Qadi Abu Muhammad al-Hasan ibn al-Hasan az-Zaydi was born not requiring circumcision. He said that this is why he was nicknamed 'the Purified' (Mutahhar). He said, "I read in his handwriting, 'Abu Muhammad al-Hasan was born purified and was not circumcised and he died as he was born." The *fuqaha'* have mentioned in their books that people born like that are not circumcised.

It is said that circumcision was one of the commands by which Allah tested His Friend, peace be upon him, and that Ibrahim completed and fulfilled them all. The people most severely tested are the Prophets, then the most exemplary, and so on. The Prophet counted circumcision as part of the *fitra*, and it more befits the state of the Prophet, peace be upon him, not to have this virtue taken from him and for Allah to have honoured him with it as He honoured His Friend. His qualities are greater and higher than the qualities of other Prophets. So it is more appropriate for the angel to have circumcised him than for it to have been one of his special attributes.

The source of the account of circumcision by the Angel is what was related by al-Khatib from Abu Bakra to the effect that Jibril circumcised the Prophet, may Allah bless him and grant him peace, when he cleansed his heart. It is *mawquf*, stopping with Abu Bakra, and its *isnad* is not sound. Al-Khatib said about it: "Abu'l-Qasim 'Abdu'l-Walid ibn 'Uthman ibn Muhammad al-Bajali told us; he was told by Ja'far ibn Muhammad ibn Nasir, who was related to by Muhammad ibn 'Abdullah ibn Sulayman, who was related to by 'Abdu'r-Rahman ibn 'Uyayna al-Basri, who was related to by Abu 'Ali ibn Muhammad al-Mada'ini, who was related to by Salama ibn Muharib from his father from Abu Bakra. This *isnad* is not one that can be used as evidence."

The *hadith* concerning the angel opening his heart is related by various paths, *marfu'* back to the Prophet, may Allah bless him and grant him peace. None of them say that Jibril circumcised him except for this *hadith,* which is *gharib* (rare) and *shadhdh* (aberrant).

According to Ibn al-'Adim, some transmissions report that the Prophet's grandfather 'Abdu'l-Mutallib circumcised him on the seventh day. He said, "On the face of it, this is most likely to be correct and is closer to the truth." It also comes by way of Ibn 'Abdu'l-Barr with an *isnad* going back to Ibn 'Abbas that 'Abdu'l-Muttalib circumcised the Prophet, may Allah bless him and grant him peace when he was seven days old. He prepared a meal on his behalf and named him Muhammad. Yahya ibn Ayyub said, "We did not find this *hadith* with anyone except Ibn Abi's-Sari – that is, Muhammad ibn al-Mutawakkil ibn Abi's-Sari – and Allah knows best."

Section 14: On the Divine wisdom in the sons of Adam being resurrected uncircumcised

Allah has promised – and He is the One who does not break His promise – that He will bring mankind back as He originated them the first time. One aspect of the truth of His promise is that He will restore people to the form in which He originated them the first time with full and complete limbs. Allah Almighty says: *"That Day We will fold up heaven like folding the pages of a book. As We originated the first creation so We shall regenerate it. It is a promise binding on Us. That is what We will do."* (21:104) The Almighty says, *"…as He originated you, so you will return."* (7:29)

In addition, circumcision was prescribed in this world to perfect purity and to keep men free from urine. The people of the Garden do not urinate or defecate and there is no impurity which can get onto the foreskin that it should need to be kept free of it. The foreskin does not prevent or impede the pleasure of intercourse. This applies if it is decreed that they shall remain in the same condition in which they are resurrected. But being resurrected like that does not mean that they will necessarily remain the same as when they were resurrected.

Mankind will be resurrected barefoot and naked, and then they will be clothed and their physique extended and it will be increased again after that: there will be increase in the physical stature of the people of the Garden and the people of the Fire. When they rise from the graves, however, they will be in the form which they had in this world and with the same attributes, forms and states, and so every slave will be resurrected as he died and then Allah will make them evolve as He wishes.

Will those foreskins which are part of their formation in the graves remain or disappear? Either is possible. There is no report about this matter. And Allah Almighty knows best.